Ben Lawers and its alpine flowers

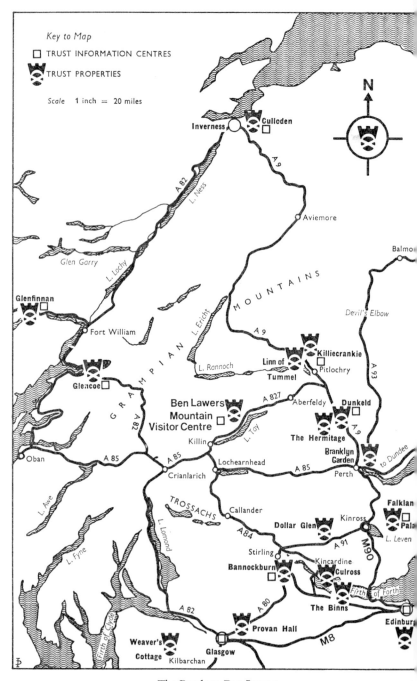

N

Inverness

Culloden

L. Ness

Aviemore

Balmo

Glen Garry

L. Lochy

A 82

Glenfinnan

Fort William

L. Ericht

MOUNTAINS

Devil's Elbow

A 9

A 9

Killiecrankie

Pitlochry

Linn of Tummel

L. Rannoch

GRAMPIAN

Glencoe

A 82

Ben Lawers Mountain Visitor Centre

A 827

Aberfeldy

Dunkeld

The Hermitage

A 9

to Dundee

Killin

L. Tay

Oban

A 85

A 85

Lochearnhead

Branklyn Garden

A 85

Perth

Crianlarich

L. Awe

TROSSACHS

Callander

A 84

Dollar Glen

Kinross

Falklan Pala

L. Leven

L. Lomond

L. Fyne

A 91

M 90

Stirling

Kincardine

Culross

Bannockburn

The Binns

Firth of Forth

A 82

A 80

Provan Hall

Edinbur

Firth of Clyde

Weaver's Cottage

Glasgow

M 8

Kilbarchan

The Roads to Ben Lawers.

Ben Lawers
and its alpine flowers

a property of
The National Trust for Scotland

Printed by R. & R. Clark, Ltd., Edinburgh
for The National Trust for Scotland
5 Charlotte Square, Edinburgh EH2 4DU

Production by Bessie Darling Inglis

Typography by Edwin A. Brown

Contents

Ben Lawers and the Trust   page 8

History and Legend. *M. S. Campbell, F.L.S.*   9

Ben Lawers Range. *Gertrude L. Elles, M.B.E., D.Sc.*   13

The Alpine Flora and Ben Lawers.
    Adapted from the text by Duncan Poore, M.A., Ph.D.   20

Notes on the Plants Illustrated. *J. Grant Roger, B.Sc., F.L.S.*   65

Animals of the Mountain. *J. Grant Roger, B.Sc., F.L.S.*   80

Ski-ing on Ben Lawers Range. *John Kerr*   83

List of Botanical Terms. *Douglas M. Henderson, B.Sc.*   85

The National Trust for Scotland   87

Plates

Ben Lawers from the road between Lawers
    and Carie   facing page 16

Meall Corranaich and Ben Ghlas from the
    south side of Loch Tay   17

Looking NNE from Ben Lawers   32

January ski-ing on Ben Ghlas   33

Maps

The Roads to Ben Lawers   Frontispiece

Geological Map of Ben Lawers District   page 14

Geological Section across Ben Lawers   17

Ben Lawers and Loch Tay   23

Botanical Illustrations

on pages 41 to 46

1 LYCOPODIACEAE
   SELAGINELLACEAE

2 POLYPODIACEAE

3 POLYPODIACEAE
   OPHIOGLOSSACEAE

4 RANUNCULACEAE
   CRUCIFERAE

5 CRUCIFERAE
   VIOLACEAE

6 POLYGALACEAE
   CARYOPHYLLACEAE
   LINACEAE

7 CARYOPHYLLACEAE
   GERANIACEAE
   OXALIDACEAE

8 ROSACEAE

9 ROSACEAE
   CRASSULACEAE

10 CRASSULACEAE
   SAXIFRAGACEAE

11 SAXIFRAGACEAE
   PARNASSIACEAE

12 ONAGRACEAE
   CORNACEAE
   POLYGONACEAE
   SALICACEAE

13 SALICACEAE
   ERICACEAE
   EMPETRACEAE

14 PRIMULACEAE
   GENTIANACEAE
   BORAGINACEAE
   SCROPHULARIACEAE
   LENTIBULARIACEAE

15 SCROPHULARIACEAE
   LABIATAE
   CAMPANULACEAE
   RUBIACEAE

16 RUBIACEAE
   DIPSACACEAE
   COMPOSITAE

17 COMPOSITAE

18 ORCHIDACEAE

19 ORCHIDACEAE

20 LILIACEAE
   JUNCACEAE

21 CYPERACEAE

22 CYPERACEAE

23 GRAMINEAE

24 GRAMINEAE

Drawings by Bessie Darling Inglis

Ben Lawers and the Trust

THE TRUST was enabled to purchase the south side of the mountains of Ben Lawers and Ben Ghlas in 1950 through the generosity of the late Mr P. J. H. Unna, who had a long association with the Scottish Mountaineering Club and with the mountains of Scotland. It was his lifelong ambition to see as much Scottish mountainside as possible preserved unspoiled and free of access to all. Through the Trust he was able to fulfil part of this ambition. He gave a substantial donation to the appeal fund with which the Trust purchased Glencoe, and he provided the entire purchase price for the Trust's acquisition of Kintail Estate in Wester Ross. Mr Unna, who died in a climbing accident on the face of Ben Aighennan near Dalmally in 1950, a few months after the acquisition of Ben Lawers, left the whole residue of his estate to the Trust, with the expressed wish that this money should be used primarily for mountainous country projects.

One of the Trust's main aims in acquiring Ben Lawers was to ensure the preservation of its alpine flora, unrivalled in the British Isles, and visitors to the mountain are expressly urged not to pick or uproot these flowers as specimens. From 1963, the Nature Conservancy combined with the Trust in establishing an Information Centre at the car park on the hill road from Loch Tay to Glen Lyon. Because of its great interest, Ben Lawers was selected as the site of a new Visitor Centre, a project made possible by grants from the Countryside Commission for Scotland, the Carnegie U.K. Trust, and Perthshire County Council. The Nature Conservancy continues to help in providing the information services.

The Centre, built of local stone and dark timber, has been designed to fit inconspicuously into the hillside landscape. It contains an exhibition telling the story of the mountain from the Ice Age to the present day, and planned to encourage the visitors' interest in countryside conservation. The story is extended to parts of the mountain by self-guided trails and guided walks.

History and Legend

IF ONE PAUSES to look back towards Loch Tay from the slopes of Ben Lawers, many signs of the past are evident. Below the head dyke the remains of old walls and ditches enclose what is often now only rough pasture for cattle and horses; and it is easy to pick out the ruins of cottages each with its small group of trees. In low evening light it can be seen that the pasture is ridged—the evidence of former cultivation—and there are broad strips between the march dykes, where animals were led to the hill between cultivated fields. Above the wall, too, are signs of earlier activity. Overgrown roads climb up to the peat beds or to groups of ruined shielings which nestle in the more fertile and sheltered situations. All this causes one to wonder what was the way of life of these people and what led to its decay.

Because of its favoured situation and fertile schist and limestone soils, Lochtayside has probably been cultivated from very early times. It is certainly rich in remains of the bronze age, and forest clearance is likely to have taken place even earlier. We can, however, only conjecture what were the agriculture and customs of these early people.

We have evidence of the ownership of Lawers itself from the middle of the 14th century when Chalmers of Lawers wrested it from the Macmillans. In 1473 it was confiscated from that family by James III and was given to Sir Colin Campbell of Glenorchy for his assistance in bringing to justice the murderers of James I, among whom was Thomas Chalmers. From that date until the present century, the lands of Lawers belonged to the Campbells of Glenorchy and Breadalbane. This constancy of ownership together with freedom from any major participation in the '15 and '45 have undoubtedly protected Lochtayside from the ravages of warfare and feud which have hindered progress in much of the Highlands, although the House of Lawers was burned and the lands plundered by Montrose in 1645.

It is possible to reconstruct the state of Lochtayside in 1769 fairly accurately from the excellent survey and maps which were made at the order of the third Earl of Breadalbane. The area was then divided into small farms which were held direct by tenants from the Earl. Parts of

9

these were sublet to crofters who co-operated in the running of the farm and supplied horses to make up the plough team of four which was used at the time. Houses were of the black house type, but, in contrast to the few extant crofters' houses, were probably devoid of real chimneys or windows, and were thatched with turf, which was removed at intervals and used as manure on the land. The House of Lawers was probably one of the few substantial houses, two storeys high and thatched with straw. The present farm houses all date from the last century. The local communities were mainly self-supporting, though their standard of living was low. Grain and flax were milled at Lawers and each township had its own tradesmen, tailors, weavers, shoemakers and smiths.

This was a transitional period in agriculture. Cultivation was still almost exclusively of oats and bear, a primitive kind of barley. Although flax had been introduced into Breadalbane as early as 1728, it was still grown in the flatter straths and there are no returns for it from Lochtayside in the survey of 1769. The flax mill must therefore have dealt with imported material. This mill was built by Ewen Cameron, who died at Lawers in 1817 at the astonishing age of 112. The mill is said to be one of the first two of its kind to be erected in the Highlands. During the succeeding years flax growing enjoyed a sudden spell of popularity, and then, as suddenly, died out. The plant is very seldom seen now in the neighbourhood, even as a weed. Neither potatoes nor turnips had yet become a field crop, though both became widespread in the next thirty years.

The same passage from the old style to the new took place about this time in transport, in stock-rearing and in general agricultural economy. In 1769 cattle were still taken out and herded through the summer at remote shielings. The introduction of black-faced sheep and the control of foxes had not yet made it possible to keep sheep on the hill. They were considered too delicate and taken in at night! Thus the hill grazings, though locally over-stocked, were not subjected to the intensive grazing right over the summits which became the rule in the next century.

The farms were managed according to the run-rig system. Each crofter cultivated a small strip of each crop instead of contributing his labour to the cultivation of large fields whose produce could be divided. Moreover, the strips were changed from year to year. The result of this was obvious: the land deteriorated because it was not profitable to expend energy on land which would pass to a neighbour.

The infield, which was usually below the road, was cropped every year and received all the manure: the outfield was cultivated until it became unprofitable and then allowed to lie fallow to recover fertility. This wasteful and inefficient system was changed in the years following the survey. In 1770 a law was passed relaxing the strict conditions on entailed estates and it became possible to let farms on long leases, which were made conditional on enclosing woodland and erecting stone walls between farms, or, where this was not possible, digging ditches 6 ft. deep and 10 ft. wide! Strict conditions were also attached to the manuring and rotation of crops. After this the countryside began to take on its present aspect.

Fuel was something of a problem in the days before the railway made economic the importation of coal. Tenancy of a farm carried with it the right to collect firewood and cast peats, but both of these took time and the peat was scarce and far away. The old peat roads can still be traced to the edge of the bogs and some of them go up to at least 2,000 ft. The writers of the *Old Statistical Account* complain both of the waste of time and the wear and tear to carts engaged in carrying peat. Communications, too, were difficult. The present road along the north side of the loch was built by the third Earl of Breadalbane to join up the two existing Wade roads at Kenmore and Glendochart. The old village of Lawers, the ruins of whose house, mill and church can still be seen, was by the shore of the loch and its main connection was by ferry with Ardtalnaig.

In the next century the increased efficiency of farming, the more peaceable nature of the times and the vaccination against smallpox all contributed to over-population. To combat this the fourth Earl made the suggestion that sheep should be banished and that the people should be supported by more intensive cultivation of arable land. Unfortunately the opposite counsel prevailed and some evictions took place, though on a much smaller scale than in much of the Highlands.

The extension of sheep-walk and improved communications have led here, as elsewhere in the Highlands, to depopulation and a reduction of the area under the plough. Many crofters' cottages have become derelict during the past thirty years. The influx of hydro-electric labour into the neighbourhood has produced renewed activity.

The House of Lawers seems to have been the home of the famous Lady of Lawers. The identity of this lady is uncertain, but she is believed to have been a Stewart of Appin. She lived in the middle of the 17th century, and it was during her lifetime that the old church of Lawers, which replaced the pre-Reformation foundation near the graveyard, was built. She was a famous seer and is credited with many prophecies about the decline in prosperity, the evictions and other matters, which have since come true, although other events which she forecast have not yet come to pass. Many other tales persisted locally until recently: the shooting of a witch with a silver sixpence by the blacksmith MacMartin; the origin of Loch Tay from a spring in the west corrie of Ben Lawers, which was a milkmaid inadvertently left open after watering her cows; and the tale of the last illicit still at Tomocrocher. These are tales which are recounted fully elsewhere.

The mountains of Breadalbane have long been famous for their alpine flora. They are frequently mentioned in Lightfoot's *Flora Scotica*, with records in the name of the Rev. Mr Stuart, minister of Killin. In these early records it was the surrounding hills, not Ben Lawers, that were mentioned. In *Mountain Flowers* John Raven and Max Walters recorded that the wealth of the Ben Lawers flora was first discovered by James Dickson, when he visited the mountain in 1789, and that it was he who first discovered *Saxifraga cernua* when he visited Lawers for the second time in 1792. The names of Dr Robert Townson, George Don, Robert Brown, Professor Babington and the great Perthshire botanist Dr Buchanan-White are among the many famous names to be associated with the mountain.

Nature conservation, moreover, is no novelty in the area. As early as 1600 Sir Duncan Campbell of Glenorchy encouraged the planting of trees by tenants, and supplied saplings of oak, ash and plane (probably sycamore) at two pennies apiece. At the same time heavy fines were imposed on wanton destruction of trees.

The National Trust for Scotland, in co-operation with such notable allies as the Nature Conservancy, the Countryside Commission for Scotland and the Carnegie U.K. Trust is doing its utmost to care for the mountain and its unique flora.

Ben Lawers Range

BEN LAWERS belongs to the Breadalbane region of the Central Highlands, and may be regarded as the culmination of the mountain range that skirts the north side of Loch Tay. Judged by British standards this is an area of considerable elevation, Ben Lawers itself reaching an altitude of 3,984 ft., and the range having several summits exceeding 3,000 ft. It is deeply dissected by many glens, of which the most important is the Lochan na Lairige Pass leading over to Glen Lyon, and many sections are exposed in the burns and on the hillsides showing the constituent rocks and their structures.

The facts now seen and interpreted necessitate considerable modification of the views of the earlier workers in Scottish geology and appear to offer a clue to the general structure of the Highlands as a whole. This structure is exceedingly complex, and can only be considered here in broad outline; the fold is, however, regarded as the fundamental unit.

NATURE OF THE ROCKS
AND THEIR SUBSEQUENT ALTERATION
(Metamorphism)

Unlike what is found in many Highland mountains, no great mass of crystalline igneous rocks has helped to build Ben Lawers. Apart from some relatively minor basaltic sills and dykes of Permo-Carboniferous or Tertiary age, the rocks of which the mountain is composed are all of sedimentary origin, topped by a discontinuous skin of glacial drift. Their appearance at the present time is, however, very different from their original state owing to the fact that at least once in their history they have been subjected to intense heat and pressure in the processes of mountain building, in which they have been largely recrystallised.

These highly altered sediments constitute a great body of rocks known as the *metamorphic rocks*, and are referred to the Dalradian System, which forms the foundation of so much of the Highlands. They are almost certainly Pre-Cambrian in age.

In the Ben Lawers area, we can confidently rule out any idea which

13

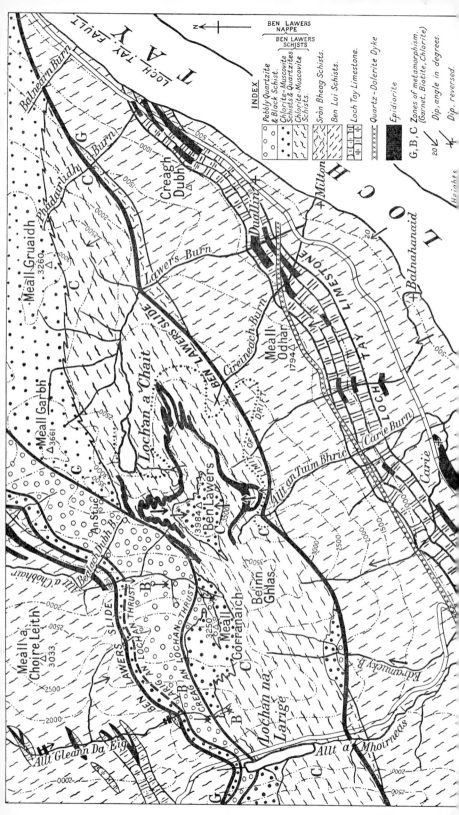

INDEX

BEN LAWERS NAPPE

BEN LAWERS SCHISTS

○○○ Pebbly Quartzite & Black Schist.

··· Chlorite-Muscovite Schists & Quartzites.

'' ' Chlorite-Muscovite Schists.

〰 Sròn Bheag Schists.

/// Ben Lui Schists.

ⅢⅢⅢ Loch Tay Limestone.

✕✕✕✕✕ Quartz-Dolerite Dyke.

███ Epidiorite.

G, B, C Zones of metamorphism. (Garnet, Biotite, Chlorite)

20↙ Dip, angle in degrees.

↗ Dip, reversed.

— Heights

postulates such metamorphic changes as due to local magmatic activity, since anything which might induce this is wholly absent. Moreover, the alteration is of a regional character, and we should follow Harker and regard the processes of Mountain Building and Regional Metamorphism as being the logical consequence of prolonged sedimentation in a slowly subsiding geosynclinal basin. The rocks became depressed into regions of higher and higher temperature wherein the higher grade of metamorphism is to be associated with deeper burial and therefore older rocks. Progressive metamorphism of this type, as affecting sediments of similar composition (mudstones, clays, etc.), shows definite index minerals belonging to increasing grades (zones) of metamorphism. Three of these belts, *e.g.* (1) Chlorite, (2) Biotite, (3) Almandine garnet, are found on Ben Lawers as characterising different grades.

The present-day conception of Metamorphism regards the Chlorite zone as belonging to the relatively outer regions of those parts of the earth's crust in which Regional Metamorphism is developed, while the Biotite and Garnet zones would belong successively to deeper regions.

If this conception of the nature and relation of the Metamorphic zones be accepted, it follows that the more intensely metamorphosed rocks were at one time those at greatest depths, so that any inversion of this order, or any break in the normal sequence of the rocks contributing what might be termed a 'metamorphic hiatus' or 'metamorphic unconformity' will require an explanation to be sought in the stratigraphical and structural relationships of the rocks over a wide area.

Finer sediments tend to be converted into schists of various kinds showing a well-developed foliation, *e.g.* layers or aggregates of new minerals which may be differently coloured, but tend to split very readily in one direction, and in their undivided state appear as if divided into parallel layers. They frequently show innumerable minor puckers and folds with every degree of contortion, *e.g.*:

CHARACTERISTIC LAYERS OF BEN LAWERS SCHISTS
ABOVE THE SLIDE

1 Chloritic schists (*green*).
2 Mica schists, with or without garnets (*silvery sheen*).
3 Garnetiferous mica schist.
4 Quartz schists, grading into quartzites by addition of higher percentage quartz and often gritty.

The quartzites may be quite crystalline and are often fairly thick; they are commonly interbedded with schists.

Geological map of Ben Lawers district

A thin though persistent grey crystalline limestone is of frequent occurrence, partly as the result of folding. This is the Loch Tay limestone.

There is a metamorphic hiatus between the lower and upper parts of Ben Lawers schists along the line of the Ben Lawers Slide by which the two rock groups constituting the mountain are divided. The rocks of the one group lie well within the Garnet zone and those of the other in the Chlorite zone.

RELATION OF METAMORPHISM TO FOLDING

This regional metamorphism is obviously intimately related to the folding of the rocks.

In the original geosyncline the sediments are subject to increasing temperature with depth, but temperature is not the sole effect. Operating over a great thickness and extent of rocks, the increasing temperature leads to expansion which necessarily calls into play powerful stresses that are partly relieved by folding and crystallisation. Folding of an extreme type affording some measure of relief is a natural accompaniment of regional metamorphism.

There is so close a connection between metamorphism and fundamental folding that the two processes must be regarded as being part of the same story, and as having taken place at approximately the same time. The effect of any later folding upon these early folds seems to show that it is unaccompanied by any constructive metamorphism, so that its effect is merely to fold or fault the early folds and metamorphic belts.

NATURE OF BEN LAWERS FOLDS

There are two main classes of folds, both of which are of the nature of earth waves: (1) *Epeirogenic or continent-making folds*, and (2) *Orogenic or mountain-making folds*. The former have the longer wave-length, but the latter often the greater amplitude, and it is with the Orogenic folds that we have to deal on Ben Lawers. Such appear to be produced as the result of tangential stresses acting mainly from one direction, upon rock sheets which have not free play but are *held* in one direction at least to a greater or lesser extent by some resistant rock mass. If the stress be comparatively slight, the earth waves are simple and reveal themselves in their fundamental form merely as a succession of arches

16

Ben Lawers from the road between
Lawers and Carie
Photo: *R. M. Adam*

and troughs known to geologists as anticlines and synclines respectively. In all such folds where the strike remains constant there must be a progressive change in the amount of inclination or dip from the outside to the inside of the fold, and the inclination of the beds changes from one direction to its opposite. There must, therefore, be an area over which there is no inclination or dip at all; this is the *axis of the fold* and the plane in which it lies is the axial plane.

The general structures may be rendered more complex by the formation of ripples on the waves, that is the existence of minor folds or buckles within the larger folds constituting what are known as anticlinoria and synclinoria. There is much folding of this type on Ben Lawers (*see Summit Syncline*). The axial planes of the fold may be perpendicular or inclined, so that the fold may be symmetrical, asymmetrical or recumbent. With relatively slight tangential stress the axes of the folds lie perpendicular to the direction of stress and the resulting folds are symmetrical, whilst with increasing force the axial planes become more and more nearly parallel to the direction of the stress, though in general they show a slight dip towards the quarter from which the tangential force has acted. Thus the folding may be symmetrical and grade almost imperceptibly into asymmetrical folding, in which the axial plane of the fold departs but little from the perpendicular and the dip of the beds is merely steeper on one side than the other. As the angle of the axial plane still further diminishes there may be developed the overturned fold or overfold, in which one limb of the fold is, as it were, more or less upside down, one side being doubled over the other, so that the beds are in inverted order on the lower limb of the arch or the upper limb of the trough.

In certain cases of overfolding the wave-length may be very short relatively to the amplitude, the folds being closely packed; and the inclination of successive folds may be considerable and constant in direction, so that the dip of the beds is in the same direction and equal

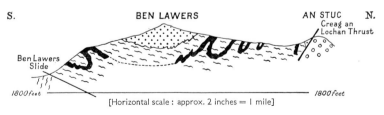

[Horizontal scale : approx. 2 inches = 1 mile]

Geological Section across Ben Lawers

17

Meall Corranaich and Ben Ghlas
from the south side of Loch Tay
Photo: W. S. Thomson

in amount on both sides of the fold (concertina folding). These are isoclinal folds and are seen very clearly in some sections on Ben Lawers. They are usually small-scale folds in which the dip of the beds is fairly high.

In other cases the axial plane approaches the horizontal and the rock sheets forming the fold are also apparently almost horizontal. Such are known as recumbent folds. They are usually regional in character, and, having an enormous wave-length, occupy considerable tracts of country. Structures of this type must often be postulated in the Scottish Highlands in order to explain the varying dips of the beds and their position both above and below each other, one set being obviously inverted.

The study of the metamorphic conditions of the beds and their mutual relations in the Scottish Highlands appears to show very conclusively that the fundamental folding of the entire region was of the nature of large-scale recumbent folding. This is evidenced not only by large-scale inversions of the actual beds but by the mutual relationships shown by the different metamorphic zones.*

An inverted order of the metamorphic belts is found throughout the district except when right up against the rocks of the Ben Lawers range, and this change seems to be connected with the existence of the Ben Lawers Slide, above which the rocks have been moved so that they no longer occupy their proper place in the metamorphic succession.

On the north side of Glen Lyon, the beds are in normal sequence so that they must belong to a different limb of the great fold from that seen on the Lawers range, namely the lower instead of the upper limb of the great Ben Lui fold.

FOLDING

In all cases of folding or overfolding another factor may have to be considered, and that is the bending power of the rocks affected at the depth of the formation of the fold. Sooner or later the limit of bending or folding may be reached, and the folded rock breaks with the formation of fold faults. In extreme cases these may constitute veritable *slides* (Bailey) along which, if the tangential force be continued and transmitted, portions of the broken fold may be driven forward for many miles. (In their *effects* such faults are similar to reversed faults of

* *Metamorphism in Relation to Structures in the Scottish Highlands,* Elles and Tilley.

the thrust type, but as regards their *origin* they represent the highest power of folding. At any subsequent time the fault plane or slide and its rock burden may themselves be further folded.) The thrust mass or Nappe is the sheet of rock that has moved forward on the top of the thrust or slide.

The whole of the Ben Lawers Nappe above the Ben Lawers Slide is a maximum structure of this type.

CLASSIFICATION OF SOME OF THE FOLDS ON BEN LAWERS

MAXIMUM: Ben Lawers Nappe.
              Inversion of beds in recumbent folds. Ben Lawers district.

MAJOR: Ben Lawers summit Syncline. (*See Minor and Minimum.*)
              Creag an Lochan Anticline.
              Meall Corranaich Syncline.

MINOR: Isoclinal folding Cireinaich Burn. (*See diagram.*)

MINIMUM: Puckering, Meall Corranaich Syncline.

CONCLUSION

It will therefore be realised that the structures developed in a rock mass are determined by its physical properties and the system of forces that acts upon it.* Moreover, what is seen in any locality depends upon the position in the fold or folds from which it is in view. The dominant factor in any one area may be merely one series of isoclinal folds; but similar isoclinal folds when viewed over a larger area may appear as part of a much more important structure.

It cannot be urged too strongly that how much of the structure is exhibited depends upon the place and direction of the ground traversed. The whole is rarely, if ever, visible, and as a rule has to be pieced together from different places. To grasp the development of the maximum structure (for example recumbent folding) it may be necessary to cover a wide region including several glens in order to appreciate that the beds are as often upside down as right way up (one set being reversed).

All these structures may be detected in the Ben Lawers region (*see table*) and many in other regions of the Highlands. They may, indeed, probably be regarded as a characteristic feature of many great mountain chains of which Ben Lawers is but a fragment of one.

       ★ *Outlines of Structural Geology*, E. Sherbon Hills.

The alpine flora and Ben Lawers

BEN LAWERS, amongst professional and amateur botanists alike, is a name to conjure with because of the richness of its alpine flora, and it is rightly looked upon as the botanists' Mecca. Everyone with a true enthusiasm for British mountain plants pays it at least one visit in a lifetime; and there are few who are not impelled to return again and again. Many climb the mountain simply to enjoy the delicate beauty of its alpine flowers, but to the botanist of enquiring mind Ben Lawers offers many fascinating problems. Why, for instance, out of all the array of hills in the Scottish Highlands, should the Ben Lawers range have such an abundance of flowers; and why should the hills of Bread-albane be green hills, contrasting so sharply with the purple and brown hills of Rannoch and Atholl? While possessing many features common to all the higher British mountains, in both flora and vegetation Ben Lawers is in a sense unique.

The nature of any vegetation depends primarily on climate and soil, and that is where we must begin. Soil as well as vegetation is broadly determined by climate; and soil and vegetation interact closely.

CLIMATE

The effects of climate are indivisible, but it is convenient to consider them in two parts. First, there is the general climate of the region, which has an over-all determining effect on the vegetation and controls the differences between Perthshire and, say, the south of England. Second, there is the local climate affecting this small area and relative to the rest of the region, for example, the difference between lowland and mountain-top, and between exposed ridge and sheltered corrie. Both general and local climates influence the distribution of plants in two ways. There are direct influences including damage by frost, wilting and death from excessive dryness, and inability to flower and set seeds because of low temperatures; there are also indirect influences which include waterlogging of the soil and washing out of essential plant nutrients by rainfall.

The rainfall of the lowlands around Lawers is moderate, but the change from east to west is rapid and amounts to about an inch more rain per annum for every mile one goes west. Whereas Aberfeldy has an average rainfall of only 38·7 ins. a year, the average for Killin is 56·8 ins. The rainfall at Lawers itself is probably about 45 to 50 ins. In the British Isles a rainfall of 50 to 55 ins. appears to be an important level for vegetation, for throughout the country at places with a rainfall above this the soil is so frequently leached and waterlogged that the growth of bog is favoured. The area of Lawers is just below the critical amount of rainfall. One of the main grievances of the local people at the end of the 18th century was, in fact, that fuel for peat was so scarce and far away. The transition between the moderately dry grassy hills to the east of Killin and the bog-covered slopes of Glenlochay and Glendochart is impressively rapid. Bog growth in the Lawers neighbourhood is confined to small, waterlogged hollows on the low ground, and in the hills to areas of gently-sloping, impermeable boulder-clay where the drainage is impeded. Rainfall increases with altitude, and it may well be that on these flats between 1,900 and 2,100 ft. the rainfall is above 55 ins. In the absence of rain-gauges at high altitudes in Breadalbane, it is possible to give only an estimate of what the rainfall may be on the top of Ben Lawers, but although certainly much higher than 45 ins. it will not approach the figure of 170·8 ins. which is the average annual rainfall on the summit of Ben Nevis.

The main influence of rainfall on vegetation in British mountains is through its effect on the soil, and through atmospheric humidity and the prevalence of cloud. Atmospheric humidity is high on mountain-tops: on Ben Nevis the humidity averages 94 per cent saturation with water vapour, but during hot summer days on exposed mountain-tops this may drop to very low levels, causing the mosses to appear grey or yellow-brown and the lichens to break up underfoot. Mountain plants must be able to live through both extremes.

TEMPERATURE

The altitude of Perth is 76 ft. There the average mean temperature is above 50° F. for five months of the year, 58·8° F. for July, the hottest month. The average mean temperature for January, the coldest month, is 37·7° F. As you rise in altitude the temperature drops at a rate of about 1° F. for every 300 ft. The temperature at Ben Lawers Hotel may thus be reckoned to be about 2° F. lower, and on the top of Ben

Lawers 13° F. lower than at Perth. At 3,000 ft. the mean monthly temperature is above 40° F. only during the five warmest months of the year. In consequence, characteristic lowland plants are replaced at high levels by others which can better withstand the more extreme temperatures and shorter growing season. This can readily be seen when walking up the mountain, the exact zonation varying with the route followed. If you climb direct to the summit up the south face you pass first through a belt of rough but fertile pasture with abundant bracken on to a bare grassland of mat-grass, *Nardus stricta*, and moor rush, *Juncus squarrosus*. At about 2,750 ft. you come to a grassland which is abundantly mixed with the lovely palmate, silver-edged leaves of alpine lady's mantle, *Alchemilla alpina*, which in July is coloured yellow-green by its flowers. Above this again the vegetation becomes more sparse, the ground more rocky, and vascular plants become fewer. Here are found the least willow, *Salix herbacea*, with horizontal branches half-buried in the soil and tiny leaves and catkins at ground level, spiked wood-rush, *Luzula spicata*, and fir clubmoss, *Lycopodium selago*. The ground between these plants is bare or covered with a dark green skin of tiny mosses, liverworts and ground lichens. Temperature alone does not determine the zones, but with increasing height lowland plants drop out, and others, characteristic of the tops, appear.

Temperature is certainly one of the most important factors limiting the altitude at which lowland plants can survive, and plants at their maximum altitude may be found badly frosted after a warm period in early spring has stimulated them to premature growth. Pearsall gives an excellent example of the changes in the moor rush with altitude. The length of flower-stalks, the number of flowers and the number of mature capsules all decrease, until at about 2,700 ft. seeds are very rarely set, although the plant may occur up to 1,000 ft. higher.

It is not quite clear whether the opposite is generally true, that alpine plants cannot grow at low altitudes because they cannot stand the heat, but certain species such as alpine forget-me-not, *Myosotis alpestris*: hoary whitlow grass, *Draba incana*; *Salix herbacea*; reticulate willow, *Salix reticulata*; mountain avens, *Dryas octopetala*, will thrive, produce flowers and seed in gardens at low altitudes where they cannot survive in the wild. Some, however, such as mountain sorrel, *Oxyria digyna* and *Alchemilla alpina* do descend to lower levels and may occur in such situations as river shingles down to 400 ft. or less. Mossy cyphel, *Cherleria sedoides*, grows on shingle at sea-level near Montrose. Probably

Ben Lawers and Loch Tay. *Iain Dunn*

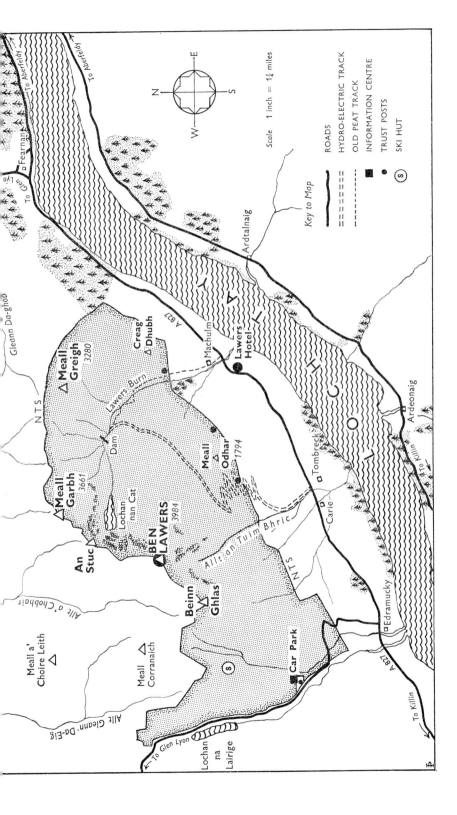

some species cannot survive higher temperatures; others are unable to compete with larger, more vigorous lowland plants, but evidence is lacking.

WIND

One of the most obvious factors of high mountain climate is wind. Winds are more frequent and violent: the change between exposed and sheltered places is more abrupt. A large boulder or summit cairn may give almost complete protection from a gale, consequently, the effects of wind on plant cover in the mountains are very noticeable. The exposed crests have a sparse vegetation of wind-resistant plants which can also tolerate wide extremes of temperature. Characteristic of the Lawers range is the *Rhacomitrium* heath, a carpet of the woolly-fringe moss, *Rhacomitrium lanuginosum*, with mountain sedge, *Carex bigelowii*, and a few lichens. The shoots of the moss usually point away from the quarter from which the prevailing wind blows. On the north-west face of Ben Lawers, a little below the summit, parts of the moss mat have been ripped off by the wind, exposing bare, stony soil. In time the moss on the windward side grows over this patch, eventually to be blown away again, a cycle of growth and erosion. Where the wind is stronger there are only small tufts of *Rhacomitrium* struggling for existence behind small rocks which give just the necessary shelter and no more. Under less extreme conditions the effect of wind shows in the short, even appearance of the turf, as on the east ridge between 3,000 and 3,500 ft. In any small hollow, or in the lee of a boulder, plants are taller and more luxuriant. In some places, notably the south-east spur running down from the east ridge towards Meall Odhar, the ground is stepped and each step has a graded intensity of wind which is strongest on the very edge, on which is found the little grass-like rush, *Juncus trifidus*, characteristic of the windswept Cairngorm plateau. The zone can be recognised from a long way off by the orange colour of the leaf-tips of the rush, scorched by the wind. Good examples of the local influence of strong wind can be seen also on the floor and sides of the south-west corrie, where there are small knolls with a wrinkled, blackened surface carrying a sparse vegetation of *Vaccinium* spp. (blaeberry and cowberry), and dwarf cudweed, *Gnaphalium supinum*, in sharp contrast to the luxuriant, green grassland full of alpine flowers which surrounds them. In winter these knolls are blown free of snow and are open to the icy blast of the wind, whereas the surrounding hollows are insulated under a blanket of snow.

24

In the mountains it is impossible to dissociate the effects of exposure and snow-cover, for wherever the force of the winter wind drops, snow falls and forms drifts. The main drifts always form, therefore, in the lee of a ridge. In general the biggest drifts form on the north-east side because of the greater frequency and strength of south-west winds. Saddles are often the most exposed localities on mountains, for the wind is canalised in the corries on either side. Drifts frequently form below the crest on both sides of a pass.

Snowfall in the Scottish Highlands is most irregular. The first snow of the autumn usually falls early in September, but frequently the hills are not well covered until after Christmas. The last snow may disappear from Ben Lawers as early as April but often some remains until June or even July. Small snow showers may occur in any of the summer months, although they are not common. In this irregularity of snow-cover the British hills differ from the Scandinavian hills and the Alps, where the seasons are more sharply defined and the snow-cover is more stable. In this country there is only a small difference between the summer and winter mean temperatures, and the latter fluctuates round about freezing point, so that even in the middle of winter, rain may fall and the snow melt on the mountain-tops.

SOIL

It is perhaps not generally realised that both soils and vegetation develop, so that a piece of ground left alone over a long period of time, would show a succession of types of soil and of vegetation. Finally, within limitations imposed by the topography and the parent rock, a soil and vegetation suited to the particular climate of the region would develop, which would be relatively stable. Ecologists call these respectively the climax soil type and the climax vegetation. In this development soil and vegetation proceed in step with one another. The primitive soil is thin and its vegetation lowly, often consisting only of mosses and lichens, whereas the climax soil is deep and very often covered with forest. The vegetation plays a vital part in the development of the soil, by the action of its roots, by deposition of humus on the surface in which a population of bacteria, fungi and soil fauna may live, and by providing protection from erosion. As the fertility of the soil increases it can support a heavier crop of plant life. In mountainous regions primitive soils and early stages of plant succession are common, due to the instability of the habitat, where new rock surfaces are constantly being exposed for soil formation.

The basic material of all soils is weathered rock, the chemical composition of which influences at least the earlier stages of soil formation. It also profoundly affects the nature of the plant communities which succeed, for species of plants differ greatly from one another in their food requirements. As soil development proceeds, both soil and vegetation become less dependent on the original parent material, to a point where resemblances develop between soils and vegetation arising from different types of rock.

The two geological formations which occupy considerable areas within the Trust property are the Ben Lawers schist and the glacial drift. There are a number of different strata of schists (*see page* 15), unusually rich in the minerals required by plants and weathering rapidly to form new soils. Glacial drift consists of clay, sand and gravels, which have been scoured from the surrounding district by glaciers and deposited by the ice itself or by glacial rivers. They vary in constitution but are more acid and more impermeable than the schists. Primitive soils formed on these geological formations differ greatly from one another, but more mature soils are very similar.

SOIL IMPOVERISHMENT

Under the climate of Ben Lawers there is a process of soil impoverishment, and very briefly what happens is this. Plant remains falling on top of the soil form a layer of humus, rain water which passes through this becomes charged with various acids, and then, in percolating downwards, removes the soluble salts which are the principal plant foods. Nitrates and the bases, calcium, sodium and potassium, and the soluble phosphates go first, then, without calcium, iron also becomes mobile. At this stage characteristic changes appear in the colour of the soil and clearly marked separate layers can be seen. Below the humus a bleached, ash-grey layer appears, from which all the iron has been washed out and deposited lower down as a red-brown zone. Finely divided humus is also carried down and forms a layer above the iron. You now have what is known as a *podsol* in which the soil has the following layers: (1) a surface layer of humus; (2) a layer of peat-stained sand; (3) bleached grey sand; (4) a brownish layer of humus and sand; (5) a red-brown iron accumulation layer; (6) the parent material. This process results in the surface soil, and consequently its vegetation, becoming steadily poorer. The rusty-red colour of iron in the soil or drainage water is a sure sign that the soil is lime-deficient; the presence of a *podsol profile*, that the impoverishment has gone further.

Podsols are common on Lawers, under much of the *Nardus* grass-land or heaths and grasslands of the high ridges, wherever soils are stable. Plant communities on podsols over Ben Lawers schist differ little from those of more acid geological formations in Breadalbane.

PEAT FORMATION

If the soil is constantly waterlogged and its surface acid, peat bog may begin to form. The chief agents are the various species of *Sphagnum*, bog moss, which owing to their peculiar sponge-like structure and low mineral requirements can exist on rain-water alone. Their dead remains, being waterlogged, do not totally decay but form peat which may carry the ground surface far above the level of mineral ground-water. Under these conditions only a few species of bog plant can survive. The growth of bog may be started by the formation of a podsol, when the iron layer may form an impermeable pan and cause the soil to become waterlogged.

FLUSHED SOILS

In contrast to these poor soils there are many on Ben Lawers in which *leaching*, the draining away of food materials, is compensated by enrichment, either by deposits of newly weathered rock particles or irrigation by water which has passed through rock and carries soluble salts. Cliff ledges, for instance, are constantly supplied with salts by water flowing over the rock surface, and, in addition, the soil is augmented by rock fragments flaking off from above. The *creep soils* at the foot of cliffs or below screes are the same, and maintained by this process in a perpetual state of immaturity. These are called *dry flushes*.

Where the ground-water rises near the surface, or wells out of it, *wet flushes* are found. The position in which they are found is often determined by a dip in the strata. Wet flushes usually bear a rich vegetation of sedges and rushes and often the flushing is seasonal only, when the snow melts. In summer they can be recognised only by a zone of more luxuriant vegetation and by layers of silt in the soil. Intermediate between wet and dry flushes are places by the sides of little burns which are periodically flooded and covered with silt. Flushing is naturally more common on the steeper slopes of the corries and occurs particularly in three areas—the floor of the south-west corrie, the north-east corrie at about 2,750 to 3,000 ft. and the north-west face at about 3,250 ft.

Most characteristic of the tops of Ben Lawers and Ben Ghlas are soils which are maintained in an immature state by the action of frost. They are of great intrinsic interest and are related to a different climatic group, the arctic tundra soils. They normally contain a large proportion of water, and, when thawing out in spring, swell up and become viscous. In this condition they can readily flow downhill, even on gentle slopes, over the still-frozen subsoil or underlying rock. Alternate freezing and thawing brings stones to the surface so the apparently stony surface of the tops of many Scottish mountains often conceals a soil 2 to 3 ft. deep, much less stony than its appearance would suggest. Under constant churning by frost no leaching is possible, and the soils are, therefore, relatively rich in basic minerals. The *solifluction*, soil creep, caused by frost action, is easily recognised by small terraces which contour the slope. These are particularly abundant all over the upper part of the north face of Lawers. They appear to be formed when the soil, which underneath the thin skin of vegetation behaves like tar or treacle, is restrained in its downward flow by a group of large plants or a rock. Occasionally the soil breaks through the crust of vegetation and a small landslide results, burying the existing plant life. The solifluction soils on Lawers are covered by particular kinds of vegetation, sparse and not beautiful, but interesting because of the extreme conditions under which they manage to survive. The black crust is composed mainly of small liverworts and mosses, principally the minute liverwort *Gymnomitrium concinnatum*. Even this is often stunted and badly developed. Vegetation cover gives some protection against soil creep, both by binding the soil and lessening the heat exchange between soil and air, so that once some larger plants are established it becomes progressively easier for others to grow. The slopes seem to remain unchanged over long periods of time by alternate cycles of destruction and development.

Other evidence of solifluction can be seen on Trust property. There are many large stones lying with their long axes down the slope and a deep trough in the ground above them. This trough appears because the stone, being heavier, moves faster than the surrounding soil. Stones of varying sizes produce other phenomena. On flat ground in the Arctic stone polygons are common. The stones are sorted by frost heaving so that the larger ones become arranged in a honeycomb pattern of polygons, while the smaller lie inside the cells formed by the larger. Polygons are rarely found in Britain, but a few examples can be seen on the broad, flat area of the east ridge of Lawers at about 3,300 ft. Here the polygons are quite small, about 1 ft. to 18 ins. across, and the pattern of the underlying stones is shown by different plants; least willow and mountain sedge marking the coarse material, and small liverworts the finer sand in the middle. On steeper slopes, a few yards to the north, the polygons are elongated, forming parallel stripes.

VEGETATION ON GLACIAL DRIFT

The area covered by glacial drift stretches from the southern boundary of the Trust property to an altitude of from 2,500 to 2,600 ft., except for Meall Odhar and some of the south-facing spurs of both Ben Lawers and Ben Ghlas. Its boundaries are shown on the map on page 14. Because of its relative impermeability the drift is now mainly covered with two types of plant community which favour moist to waterlogged soils, *Nardus* grassland and bog on deep peat.

WOODLAND HISTORY

Most of this drift area was probably at one time covered with wood-land. The few trees just below 1,700 ft. remaining on Meall Odhar are the remnants of a group of planted pines. The ancient extent of wood-land on present bog soils can be judged by remains preserved in the peat. Remains are apparently very rare above 2,000 ft., but have been found as high as 2,100 ft. in the Monadhliath, and in Breadalbane, at 2,200 ft. in Coire Riadhail north of Meall nan Tarmachan. Un-fortunately the main peat bogs on Lawers are above this height and are thus unlikely to reveal any evidence. These bogs have not revealed any traces either of birch or rowan, species which usually extended higher than the upper limit of pine. Both rowan and juniper occur at present on the bottom of the cliffs of An Stuc.

Without any factual evidence, it is rash to speculate on the composi-tion of the wood which must once have covered the southern slopes of these hills. The following facts, however, suggest that the south sides of Ben Lawers and Ben Ghlas were not covered by pure pine wood: (1) the relatively rich nature of the drift and its dampness, pine normally grows on more porous, acid drift; (2) the number of woodland species in the present-day grassland which do not usually grow amongst pine, and the absence of the species which do; (3) the absence of any large areas of podsols, which would have developed as a result of pine cover.

Judging from the present-day behaviour of the various trees, it is probable that the slopes were covered for some way up by a mixed woodland of oak, birch, and possibly ash and elm, with alder and willow in the wetter places, and at a higher level by birch and rowan. Pine may have grown in drier spots. The present grasslands, improbable as it may seem, should undoubtedly be thought of as the relics of a woodland flora modified by felling and grazing.

NARDUS GRASSLAND

Except where there is peat bog, all the south face of Ben Lawers, Ben Ghlas and Meall Corranaich is covered as high as the upper limit of the drift with rough grassland. This is dominated by mat-grass, *Nardus stricta*; or heath rush, *Juncus squarrosus*. Both are characteristic of a relatively damp, base-deficient soil which often has a peaty surface, and both have a vigorous, tufted growth. The matted, tooth-like rhizomes of *Nardus* are so dense that other species can grow only in spaces between the tussocks, and the rush is little better. Both are encouraged by intensive grazing. Sheep avoid *Nardus*, which is low in mineral content and not a tasty morsel, concentrating on the richer grasses and herbs which grow with it, sweet vernal, *Anthoxanthum odoratum* bent, *Agrostis* spp.; and fescue. *Nardus* thus spreads to the further exclusion of its associates. Naturally constant grazing by sheep carries off more nitrogen, phosphates and calcium in the form of bones, wool and flesh for market, and lacking any replenishment, these grasslands can be expected to become progressively poorer. In spite of this, because of the mineral-rich material of which this drift is composed, the *Nardus* grassland on Lawers is much richer in species than, for example, that of the Southern Uplands of Scotland. The most plentiful species other than grasses are tormentil, *Potentilla erecta*, and heath bedstraw, *Galium saxatile*.

PEAT BOG

There are now no actively growing peat bogs within the Trust property: but bog growth has in the past been active in a number of places where the slope is gradual and the drainage poor. Fragments still persist on the broad shelf to the north-west of Meall Odhar between 1,750 and 2,000 ft., and between 2,250 and 2,500 ft. on Ben Lawers and Ben Ghlas on either side of Carie Burn. The last have now almost disappeared and are covered with *Nardus* and *Juncus squarrosus*, but pillars of peat stand up above the present ground level and are full of the remains of cotton grass, bog moss and heather. These indicate where they once existed, and even now the ground is wet. A few tussocks of the cotton grass, *Eriophorum vaginatum*, are almost the only living remnants of a bog flora.

In contrast, the extensive bog to the east of Lochan a Chait, although dissected by many erosion channels often 6 or 8 ft. deep, still has a number of bog species, and locally the growth of bog moss, *Sphagnum* spp., is vigorous. Here may be found in abundance the commoner bog plants: two species of cotton grass, *Eriophorum vaginatum* and *E. angusti-folium*; deer grass, *Trichophorum caespitosum*; cloudberry, *Rubus chamaemorus*, with its beautiful, large, bramble-like flowers and orange berries; and crowberry, *Empetrum nigrum*, and *E. hermaphroditum*. The dwarf cornel, *Chamaepericlymenum suecicum*, allied to the dogwood, is also found in places on this bog.

Old peat roads lead to these bogs, which must have been the nearest source of peat for the inhabitants of Lochtayside (*see page 11*). Peat cutting may have been partly responsible for their erosion, but de-generation may be a natural phase in the life of a bog.

VEGETATION ON BEN LAWERS SCHIST

The transition from the bleak moorland and *Nardus* grassland of the glacial drift to the Ben Lawers schist is both welcome and very striking. *Nardus* and *Juncus squarrosus* diminish greatly in importance and a host of arctic-alpine species appear. Especially common and distinctive are alpine lady's mantle, *Alchemilla alpina*, so abundant that it colours whole areas of turf; moss campion, *Silene acaulis*; and alpine mouse-ear chickweed, *Cerastium alpinum*. On the schists, however, there is a diversity of habitat, each with its own different group of characteristic species. These habitats follow the main divisions of topography and soil, and are: (1) leached grasslands and heaths on stable soils at high altitudes; (2) flushed grasslands; (3) wet flushes and mountain bogs; (4) scree slopes; (5) cliffs and cliff ledges; (6) springs and mountain rills.

These categories are broadly defined, and there is much variation of the vegetation within them. It is hard to draw any hard and fast distinction between them, but they give a basis for understanding the vegetation of Ben Lawers, so let us look at each in turn.

LEACHED GRASSLANDS AND HEATHS

Three main communities can be distinguished, all of them in flat or gently sloping situations. Leaching is very evident and little enrichment by mineral particles takes place. Such communities, are not confined to Ben Lawers, but can be found on many Scottish mountains.

Rhacomitrium Heath: This has already been mentioned on page 24. It occurs on the higher parts of Ben Ghlas, on the north-west of Ben Lawers and extensively on the north ridge of Meall Corranaich. It is interesting to see this community in the middle of winter when it is usually blown clear of snow by searing winds, and each browned leaf of the *Carex* bears its own banner of ice.

Nardus Grasslands: In hollows among *Rhacomitrium* heath or among the solifluction soils of the tops you can often see sharply limited patches of *Nardus stricta*. There are many of them along the path to the summit, distinguishable from a distance by their brilliant, straw-yellow colour. These patches correspond to the position of winter snowdrifts, which have protected them from gales and very low winter temperatures. There the soil is moister. These combined conditions seem to favour the presence of the patches of *Nardus*, but if the snow lies too long, *Nardus* cannot live, and liverwort communities are found instead.

Leached Grassland: The third community has abundant *Alchemilla alpina*; blaeberry, *Vaccinium myrtillus*; fescue and lichens. One of the lichens, *Cladonia rangiferina* is the so-called reindeer moss, a food plant of the reindeer in arctic regions. This community can be seen on the crest of the south-east spur of Ben Lawers and on exposed southern sites on Ben Ghlas. The small patch of *Juncus trifidus* on the south-east spur (*see page* 24) belongs to this group of communities.

FLUSHED GRASSLANDS

This category almost defies further division. In it can occur almost all Ben Lawers' rarities, often in astonishing profusion, and in many different combinations. In fact grassland is often a misnomer, for the greater part of the ground is covered with flowering plants. Amongst the grasses, which play so small a part there, the most important are viviparous fescue, bent, tufted hair-grass, and sweet vernal. In June the community is brilliant with flower, and rivals any other in the British Isles. There are cushions of campion so packed with pink flowers that the leaves can hardly be seen, the tiny green flowers of cyphel picked out with yellow stamens, the wide-open white flowers of alpine mouse-ear chickweed putting to shame those of its dowdy lowland relative, which also occurs here, and the mountain pansy, *Viola lutea*, which here, despite its name, has large purple flowers. All these plants, as well as various fine saxifrages and many other flowers, grace these flushed

32

Looking NNE from Ben Lawers: *left*, An Stuc: *centre*, Meall Garbh; *right background*, Schiehallion; *below*, Lochan a Chait. Photo: R. M. Adam

January ski-ing
on Ben Ghlas

Photo:
The Scotsman

January ski-ing
on Ben Ghlas
Photo:
The Scotsman

grasslands of the sloping sides of the corries, where there is constant enrichment by soil movement, by silting from the numerous mountain rills, and by rock particles from the cliffs. In places where the soil is more unstable and the vegetation does not cover the ground completely, the small gentian, *Gentiana nivalis*, grows. Except for a variety of vernal whitlow grass, *Erophila spathulata* var. *inflata*, and various eyebrights, *Euphrasia* spp., the gentian is the only annual species which occurs at this altitude. This is not surprising when one considers that, in order to survive, annuals must grow from seed into flowering plants and again set seeds in a few weeks. Perhaps for this reason the gentian is confined to the south side of the mountain where it can get most sunshine and warmth. On well-drained ground which is slightly leached, particularly on turf-covered scree, there is a community dominated by *Alchemilla alpina* and *Vaccinium myrtillus*.

These flushed grasslands are heavily grazed by sheep. If this grazing were removed, it is possible that the flora would become even richer and more like that of the cliff-ledges out of reach of sheep.

FLUSHES AND MOUNTAIN BOGS

On either side of some of the mountain streams and below springs there are often fan-shaped areas saturated with water. Various Monocotyledons and mosses are the commonest plants, especially the two sedges, *Carex demissa* and *Carex saxatilis*, the russet sedge, the latter being very characteristic of rich, mountain flushes. These flushes are also the habitat of some of the rarest alpine sedges and rushes, *Carex microglochin* and *Carex atrofusca*; *Juncus castaneus*, the chestnut rush; *J. biglumis*, the two-flowered rush; and, more common, *J. triglumis*, the three-flowered rush. Other plants characteristic of wet flushes are marsh arrow-grass, *Triglochin palustris*; Scottish asphodel, *Tofieldia pusilla*; and the insectivorous butterwort, *Pinguicula vulgaris*. These species owe their presence here to the continuity of suitable habitats over a long period. We have seen how leaching makes rich soils poorer in time, and how the communities of waterlogged soil gradually change into bog communities because of the growth of peat above the mineral-water level. In both cases the vegetation is replaced by other species of quite different habits. Such a change does not seem to happen in mountain flushes. Dead plant remains do not accumulate to such an extent that the flush dries out; on the contrary, oxidation and erosion by the running water appear to balance the increase from dead leaves, and the flushes remain more or less constant. The course of the streams and the position of the springs may change in time and the flush plants migrate with them. The soil under these flushes is a peat-mud, a fine humus of plant remains and silt, very rich in nutrients.

Sphagnum bogs do not occur at high altitudes as the only species of bog moss common above 3,200 ft. are not important agents of bog-growth. Where the water is more stagnant and acid than it is in the *Carex saxatilis* flushes, small bogs do occur with abundant cotton grass, *Eriophorum angustifolium*, but the peat-forming mosses are what the Scandinavians call brown mosses. Brown mosses also form the moss layer in the flushes, but the species there are different, requiring more basic minerals. Good examples of these alpine bogs occur on the broad shelf on the east ridge of Ben Lawers at about 3,300 ft. and on the col between Ben Lawers and Ben Ghlas.

SCREE SLOPES

Most of the screes composed of moderate-sized rocks have been covered with a complete carpet of vegetation. There remain only two types of habitat, which have little in common apart from the fact that both are flushed communities, very unstable gravel slides of small stones, and jumbled masses of large blocks like those on the floor and east side of the south-west corrie. The gravel slides are too unstable to support a continuous carpet of vegetation, while the interstices between the big blocks are too wide to be bridged by plants. Consequently, plant cover in both habitats is rather sparse.

The gravel slides, usually to be found in gullies among the cliffs, are kept constantly wet by seeping water. In such situations may be found such species as yellow mountain saxifrage, *Saxifraga aizoides*; mossy saxifrage, *S. hypnoides*; alpine willow-herb, *Epilobium anagallidifolium*; alpine scurvy-grass, *Cochlearia alpina*; mountain sorrel, *Oxyria digyna*; alpine pearlwort, *Sagina saginoides*; and rarely alpine sandwort, *Minuartia rubella*. Where these gravel slides are immune from grazing by sheep a richer flora may develop. Also in the gravel slides several plants occur, which in the lowlands we think of as weeds, and which until recently were thought not to be native to Britain, for example annual poa grass, *Poa annua*; common mouse-ear chickweed, *Cerastium vulgatum*; and coltsfoot, *Tussilago farfara*.

The screes of large blocks carry a specialised flora in the dark and permanently moist crevices under the boulders. Certain ferns are common here; male fern, *Dryopteris filix-mas*; lady fern, *Athyrium filix-femina*; broad buckler fern, *Dryopteris austriaca*; oak fern, *Thelypteris*

34

dryopteris; beech fern, *T. phegopteris*; and holly fern, *Polystichum lonchitis*. Ferns require a permanently wet habitat, and these crevices under the boulders are ideal. Other species which occur in these shady crevices are the golden saxifrages, *Chrysosplenium oppositifolium* and *C. alternifolium*; wood anemone, *Anemone nemorosa*; wood sorrel, *Oxalis acetosella*; and moschatel, *Adoxa moschatellina*. In the lowlands most of these are woodland plants; but *Adoxa* reaches 3,600 ft. and *Oxalis* 4,000 ft., far higher than woodland can ever have extended. Their occurrence is due to the similarity of the habitats, for both under mountain boulders and in woodland are shade, moisture and protection from extremes of temperature. On the boulders themselves grow a number of plants which are also characteristic of the cliffs.

CLIFFS AND CLIFF-LEDGES

The cliffs provide a wide variety of habitat from sunny rock faces to deep, dripping crannies, and the flora is as variable as the habitats. Almost every plant which occurs on the upper 2,000 ft. of the Ben Lawers range can find a suitable niche somewhere on the cliffs. Any list which might be given would be very long, so only a few of the more characteristic species of each type of habitat will be mentioned.

A few of the plants found on these cliffs are true cliff-dwellers, rarely found in any other habitat. Such, for example, are alpine saxifrage, *Saxifraga nivalis*, whose small rosettes of leathery leaves are usually pressed close against the rock surface, and rose-root, *Sedum rosea*. Such also are a number of ferns, the spleenworts, *Asplenium trichomanes* and *A. viride*; and the rare alpine woodsia, *Woodsia alpina*. Other species found here favour the cliffs because of the numerous pockets of rich soil which vary in depth and wetness and degree of shading, providing habitats to suit the differing needs of the species. The instability of the ledges is important too. Small successions take place on each ledge. Once plants have become established in a crack, the soil becomes deeper because their roots break up the rock and their shoots and leaves collect rock fragments which are blown by the wind or washed down by water. Humus is also added. The pitch of these ledges, however, is often steep, and penetration of the rock itself by plant roots is shallow, so that a whole small community, plants and all, may be swept off onto the slope below. This usually happens in late spring when the soil is sodden by melt water, and drifts of snow add to the weight to be supported by the ledge. Wind may assist by tearing at the curtain of moss which often hangs down from the front of the ledge. All this may not be obvious in June and July when the cliff is covered with luxuriant growth, but no one who visits these cliffs in spring can doubt that it is important in maintaining the variety of the flora, for it is not rare to find the matted remains of the vegetation of a ledge lying at the bottom of a cliff, and areas above swept bare of vegetation. Occasionally, small landslides occur; in the winter of 1951–52 the contents of a gully poured out on the slopes beneath. The cycle of erosion and succession ensures that leaching never can proceed very far, and that there are always a number of new surfaces available for recolonisation. When physical erosion has levelled out these cliffs the alpine flora of Ben Lawers will cease to exist. Another important reason for the richness of the ledges is their inaccessibility to sheep. Grazing favours those species which are tufted, producing new shoots very close to ground level, which spread vegetatively. Consequently under grazing management, grasses and sedges are likely to spread and form a close sward which makes more difficult the survival of other plants. It is probably reasonable to blame grazing for the absence of communities of *tall herbs* and alpine willows which are found in the Norwegian mountains, where sheep are absent. Something similar to these communities does occur on the cliffs of Breadalbane mountains, where there are broad, moist ledges, inaccessible to sheep. There one finds a luxuriant community of alpines mixed with such *tall herbs* as globe-flower, *Trollius europaeus*; red campion, *Silene dioica*; greater wood-rush, *Luzula sylvatica*; wild angelica, *Angelica sylvestris*; cow parsnip, *Heracleum sphondylium*; wood cranesbill, *Geranium sylvaticum*; and others. All the species of alpine willow, as well as rowan and birch, may be found on or near such ledges. Below, where sheep have free access, these species just manage to subsist as short nibbled fragments. The comparative richness of the grazed grasslands immediately below cliffs seems to be largely due to constant replenishment by seeds from above. Other grasslands, which seem otherwise identical but which are further from cliffs, have a much poorer flora.

If grazing is enough to account for the richness of the cliffs compared with the base-rich slopes below, shelter will explain their difference from the ridges and shoulders. The difference shows not only in the number but also in the kind of species. In sheltered localities are found many of the broad-leaved herbs of the mountains, *Myosotis alpestris*, *Erigeron borealis*, *Potentilla cranzii*, *Saussurea alpina*, *Sedum rosea*, *Oxyria digyna* and others. In exposed localities plants have characters which are thought to reduce water loss by transpiration, for example reduced or inrolled leaves, thick cuticle and abundant hairs. Damage by cold is also a real danger for many of these plants; *Sedum rosea* is subject to damage by late spring frosts. With such species the shelter of the normal thin cover of snow on the cliff ledges is invaluable. Two plants of *Saxifraga oppositifolia*, purple saxifrage, have been seen growing a few inches apart, one on bare, exposed rock and the other on a ledge covered with 1 to 2 ins. of snow. Both were in flower, the latter undamaged, the former discoloured, its anthers and stigmas destroyed.

SOIL CREEP AND LATE SNOW-BEDS

As already mentioned, constant disturbance by frost has two effects on the soil; it prevents serious leaching and it keeps the soil relatively rich. Minor movements occur in some communities, caused partly by frost. In other communities there is so much downward creep of the soil that no complete covering of higher plants can form. This can happen (1) in localities where exposure is very severe, (2) where there is a long period of snow cover. In general appearance the two localities will be strikingly similar, with isolated tufts of grass and flowering plants sitting in a background of stones and small liverworts. In the Alps there are a number of species of flowering plant which are almost confined to this kind of habitat. In Britain there are few: *Gnaphalium supinum*, dwarf cudweed; and *Salix herbacea* are perhaps the only ones; but on Ben Lawers a number of liverworts and mosses are confined to the snow-beds. There is also a lichen, characteristic of such habitats, green above, brilliant saffron underneath and turned up at the edges.

Communities of this kind occupy much of the bleak upper part of the north face of Ben Lawers. The small number and size of the plants growing in late snow-beds is not surprising, for they have only two or three months free of snow each year, and most of their growth and reproduction has to be carried out in this brief period. Some plants can survive if uncovered for a shorter period than this, and will even live through years when the snow does not melt at all. Liverworts have a much greater capacity for vegetative regeneration than flowering plants. On the other side of the balance-sheet, deep snow protects plants underneath it from very low temperatures. The relatively high temperatures so provided allow snow-bed plants to retain a few green winter leaves. *Saxifraga stellaris*, *Sibbaldia procumbens* and *Gnaphalium supinum*, for example, have been recorded with green leaves under deep snow in the middle of winter. This may enable them to make a quicker start in the spring.

Some of the most beautiful of the small communities on the mountains are those of the mossy springs and rills, where clear and often ice-cold water wells up from the depths. There are many kinds, each with its own dominant mosses and liverworts. It is thought that the particular dominant is controlled by the richness and temperature of the water. The flora of the side of the rills is rather similar to that of the springs. Especially characteristic are the chickweed willow-herb, *Epilobium alsinefolium*; alpine meadow rue, *Thalictrum alpinum*; the dwarf marsh marigold, *Caltha palustris* spp. *minor*; starry saxifrage, *Saxifraga stellaris*; and hairy stonecrop, *Sedum villosum*.

This brings to an end this account of plant communities, too brief to do full justice to its subject-matter. Naturally, when dealing with communities so rich, it would be impossible to give full lists; and so only particularly interesting or characteristic species have been mentioned. By looking in these habitats one may find many more; and at the same time learn much of the fascinating interplay of plants and environment.

GEOGRAPHICAL AFFINITIES AND ORIGIN

Many of the species which grow high up on Ben Lawers are to be found in either the Alps or the Arctic regions of Europe, or both. This is not the whole story, for the species included have, in fact, a number of different distribution patterns, but it is useful as a generalisation. Actually few of the rare plants on Lawers are absent from the Arctic. One absentee is mossy cyphel, *Cherleria sedoides*, which forms large cushions of tufted shoots covered with minute green flowers: this grows only in Britain, the Alps, Pyrenees and Carpathians. Another is alpine forget-me-not, *Myosotis alpestris*, one of the glories of Ben Lawers, which grows throughout alpine and sub-alpine Europe, and also in Asia and North America. On the other hand, there are a number with a wide distribution in the Arctic; to quote only a few: rose-root, *Sedum rosea*; reticulate willow, *Salix reticulata*; and most of the saxifrages, *S. cernua*, *S. nivalis*, *S. aizoides*, *S. stellaris* and *S. oppositifolia*. Outside the Arctic, however, many of these species are to be found in other widely separated mountain regions, the Pyrenees, the Caucasus, the Urals and even the mountains of North and Central America, Japan and the Himalaya.

It is very reasonable that this should be so, for the climates of these regions have something in common. In the Arctic many of these species will grow at sea-level, whereas in the Alps they grow at high altitudes. It is not surprising in view of the Arctic nature of our mountain climate, that more species with a predominantly Arctic distribution occur here than purely alpine species. Plants can be used to a limited degree as indicators of climate. The plants of Cornwall tend to be south European or Mediterranean, and the rarities of the East Anglian Breckland with its continental climate occur in east Europe and the Steppes of Asia.

There are other questions connected with the history of the Ben Lawers plants which are fascinating but controversial. How did these plants get here, and why are the various localities in which they occur separated by such long distances; for example, *Myosotis alpestris* in Breadalbane and Teesdale?

There have been two main views on this topic, opposed to one another and both supported by powerful arguments. According to one, the little enclaves of rare arctic-alpines in Breadalbane, Clova, Teesdale and elsewhere are the descendants of small colonies of plants which survived the last Ice-age on small ice-free refuges near the places where they grow at present, similar to the *nunataks* among the Arctic ice. The other view is that the whole flora was exterminated within the area covered by the ice-sheets and must have been replaced after the Ice-age by immigration from beyond the southern extension of the ice.

In recent years, due mainly to the researches of Dr Godwin and his school in Cambridge, new light has been thrown on the whole question. They find, from the examination of plant remains in deposits of various ages, that many arctic-alpine plants were widespread in England during the late glacial period, from the melting of the ice until about 8,500 B.C. Such species as *Dryas octopetala*, *Salix herbacea* and *Betula nana*, dwarf birch, have been found in numerous places and the list of species is rapidly increasing, With them were *tall herbs* and *weeds*, in fact just such a collection of species as are found on the mountain cliffs in Breadalbane. The presence of all these plants in the late Glacial period is attributed to the abundance of immature soils left by the retreat of the ice and to the climate which was sufficiently cold to exclude closed forest. As soil leaching and forest growth spread, so the arctic-alpine flora is thought to have retreated to refuges such as Ben Lawers, where both these dangers were absent, and to have remained there ever since. Certainly with the appearance of the forest they disappeared from the south.

CONCLUSION

MacNair was the first, in 1898, to point out that all the hills which were particularly rich botanically lay on the geological formation of the Ben Lawers-Caenlochan schist. This, throughout its whole length, bears numerous species which are found rarely, if at all, on the acid, surrounding strata. An adequate supply of minerals is a prerequisite of a rich flora. This is provided by the sericite schist and associated epidiorite, which produce sufficient basic salts, of calcium, magnesium, sodium, potassium and iron, as well as phosphate and sulphate. The physical condition of the resulting soil is also excellent, for the schist breaks down to form a fine sand which contains sufficient clay to be retentive of moisture. Further, the soft nature of the rocks and the steepness of the cliffs ensure that an abundant supply of fresh mineral matter is always available to compensate for losses by leaching. The physical characteristics of the rock are almost as important as the chemical.

The altitude at which the cliffs occur and their instability must have ensured that at no time during the climatic fluctuations following the arrival of these species in the Ben Lawers neighbourhood have changes in vegetation or soil gone so far that these exacting species have been ousted from their position.

The same is true of the arctic-alpine species which grow in flushes, although they derive the minerals for their nutrition indirectly from drainage water. In this case, however, the mountain climate seems to be more important than lack of competition, for in flushes at lower altitudes, which are apparently very similar, the rare species are lacking. Continuity of low temperatures and snow cover are probably responsible for the survival of these species, in addition to the richness of the rock.

We owe this unique and beautiful assemblage of flowers to a series of coincidences; to a small stratum of ideal rock on mountains which are so high that unstable habitats have existed there continuously since early in the post-Glacial period. When the small size of some of the populations is taken into account, their survival for our delight may well seem miraculous. The main enemies are sheep and human beings, and we can control the actions of both. The responsibility for the continued survival of these plants now rests in our hands.

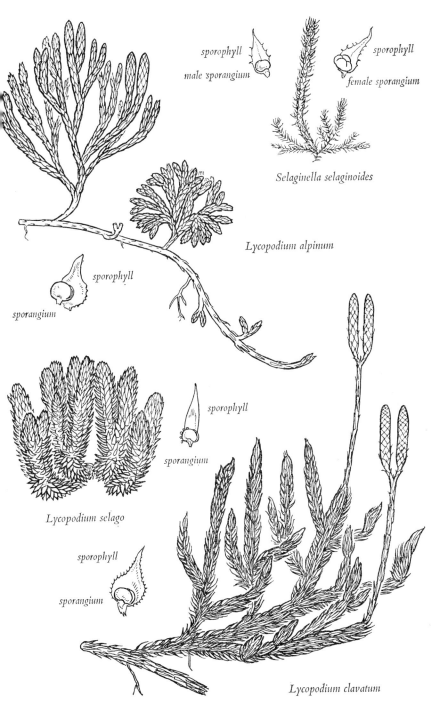

sporophyll

male sporangium

sporophyll

female sporangium

Selaginella selaginoides

sporophyll

sporangium

Lycopodium alpinum

sporophyll

sporangium

Lycopodium selago

sporophyll

sporangium

sporophyll

sporangium

Lycopodium clavatum

Fig. 1   LYCOPODIACEAE, SELAGINELLACEAE
Plants × 4/5; details enlarged.

41

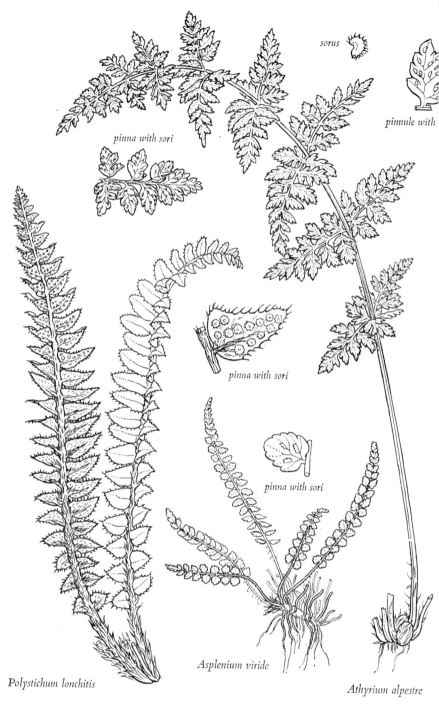

sorus

pinnule with

pinna with sori

pinna with sori

pinna with sori

Asplenium viride

Polystichum lonchitis

Athyrium alpestre

Fig. 2 POLYPODIACEAE
Plants × 4/5; details enlarged.

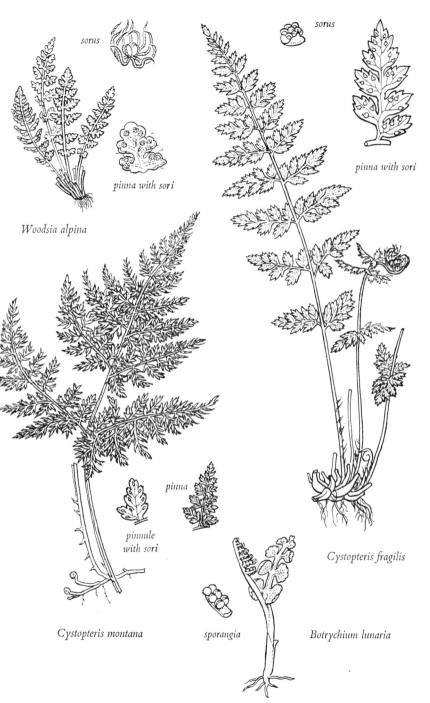

sorus

sorus

pinna with sori

Woodsia alpina

pinna with sori

pinna

pinnule
with sori

Cystopteris fragilis

Cystopteris montana

sporangia

Botrychium lunaria

Fig. 3 POLYPODIACEAE, OPHIOGLOSSACEAE
Plants × 4/5; *details enlarged.*

43

flower

Draba norvegica

Thalictrum alpinum

Draba incana

Trollius eurapaeus

Fig. 4 RANUNCULACEAE, CRUCIFERAE
Plants × 4/5; details enlarged.

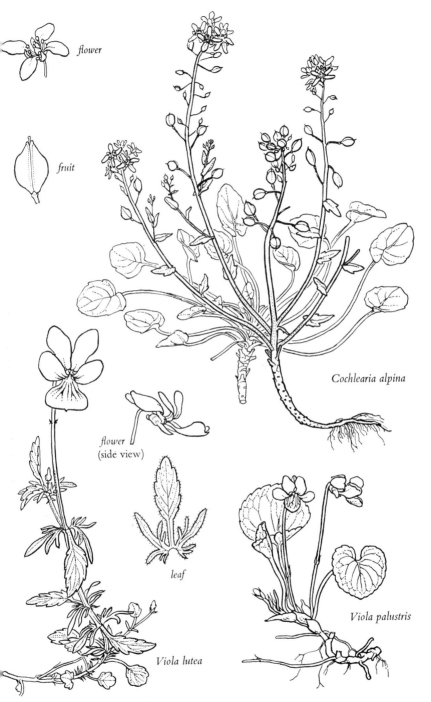

flower

fruit

Cochlearia alpina

flower
(side view)

leaf

Viola palustris

Viola lutea

Fig. 5   CRUCIFERAE, VIOLACEAE
Plants × 4/5; details enlarged.

45

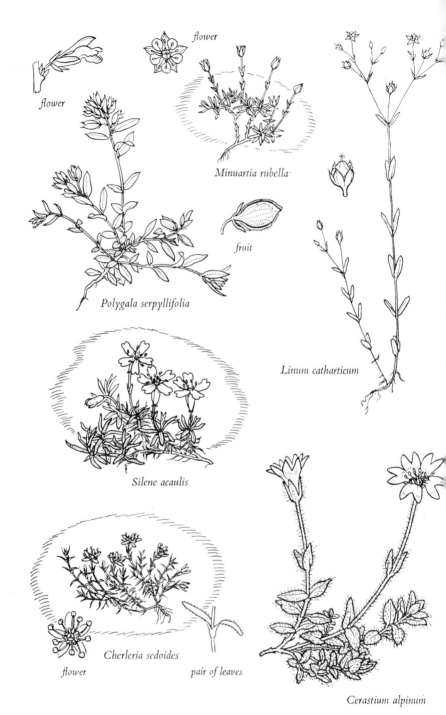

flower

flower

flower

Minuartia rubella

Polygala serpyllifolia

fruit

Linum catharticum

Silene acaulis

Cherleria sedoides

flower

pair of leaves

Cerastium alpinum

Fig. 6 POLYGALACEAE, CARYOPHYLLACEAE, LINACEAE
Plants × 4/5; details enlarged.

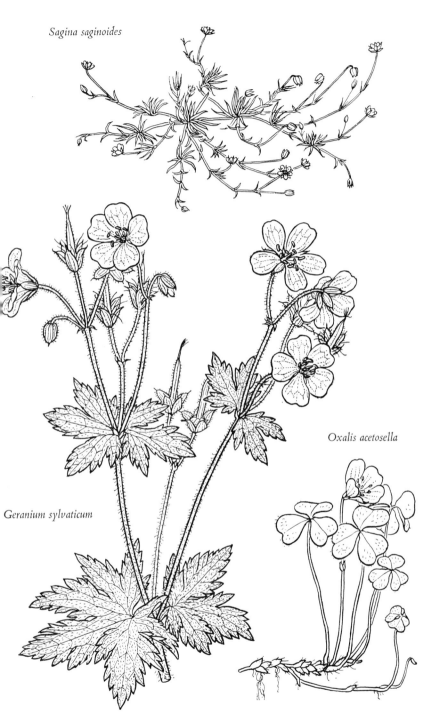

Sagina saginoides

Oxalis acetosella

Geranium sylvaticum

Fig. 7   CARYOPHYLLACEAE, GERANIACEAE, OXALIDACEAE
Plants × 4/5; *details enlarged.*

47

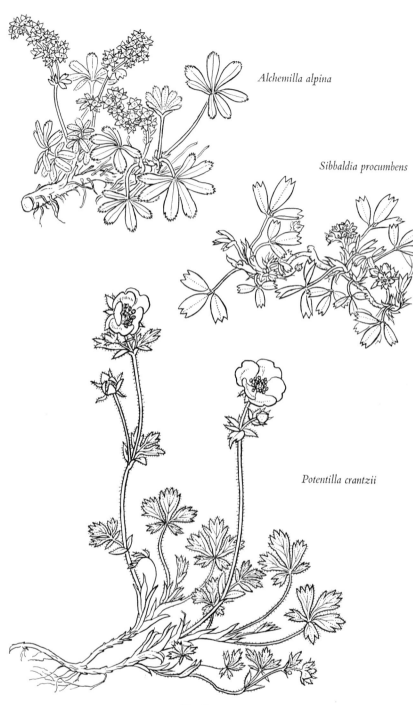

Alchemilla alpina

Sibbaldia procumbens

Potentilla crantzii

Fig. 8 ROSACEAE
Plants × 4/5; details enlarged.

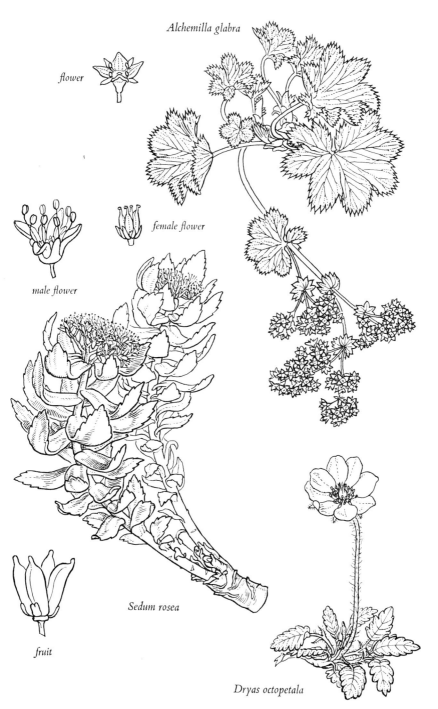

Alchemilla glabra

flower

female flower

male flower

Sedum rosea

fruit

Dryas octopetala

Fig. 9   ROSACEAE, CRASSULACEAE
Plants × 4/5; details enlarged.

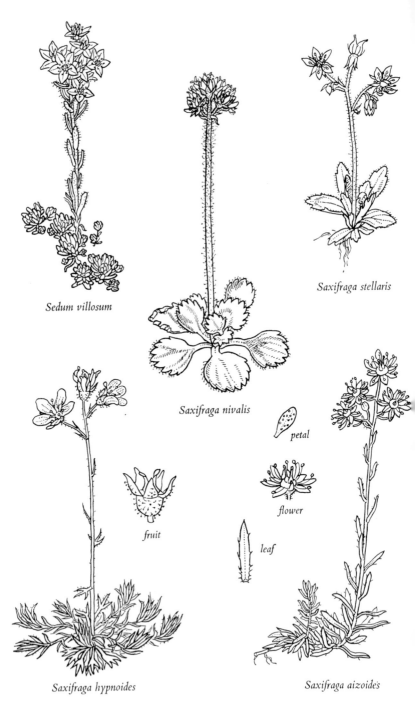

Sedum villosum

Saxifraga stellaris

Saxifraga nivalis

petal

fruit

flower

leaf

Saxifraga hypnoides

Saxifraga aizoides

Fig. 10   CRASSULACEAE, SAXIFRAGACEAE
Plants × 4/5; details enlarged.

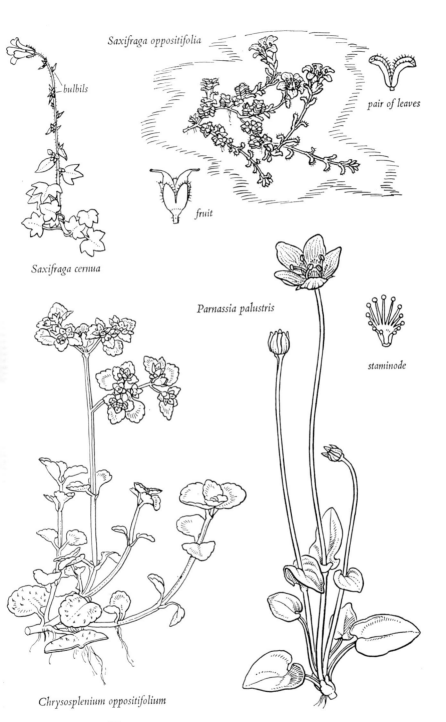

Saxifraga oppositifolia

bulbils

pair of leaves

fruit

Saxifraga cernua

Parnassia palustris

staminode

Chrysosplenium oppositifolium

Fig. 11 SAXIFRAGACEAE, PARNASSIACEAE
Plants × 4/5; details enlarged.

51

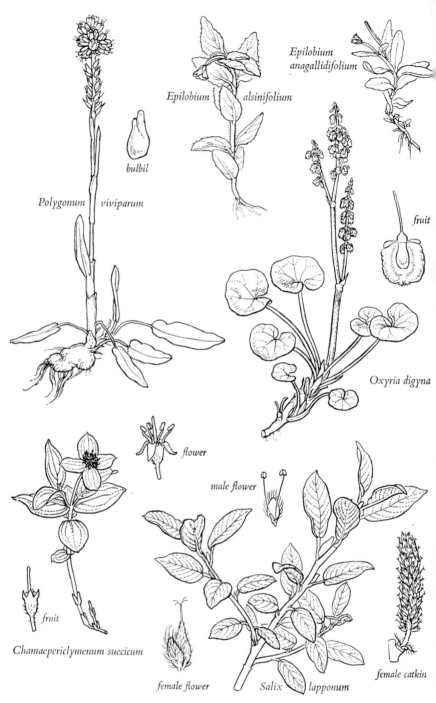

Epilobium anagallidifolium

Epilobium alsinifolium

bulbil

Polygonum viviparum

fruit

Oxyria digyna

flower

male flower

Chamaepericlymenum suecicum

fruit

female flower *Salix lapponum*

female catkin

Fig. 12 ONAGRACEAE, CORNACEAE, POLYGONACEAE, SALICACEAE
Plants × 4/5; details enlarged.

52

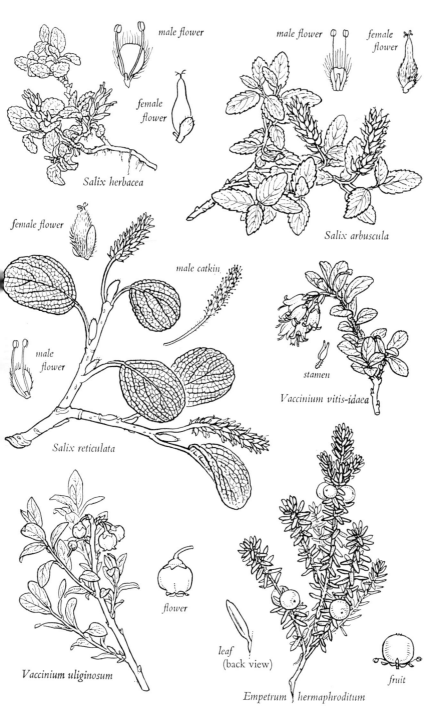

male flower

female flower

Salix herbacea

male flower

female flower

Salix arbuscula

female flower

male catkin

male flower

Salix reticulata

stamen

Vaccinium vitis-idaea

flower

Vaccinium uliginosum

leaf
(back view)

Empetrum hermaphroditum

fruit

Fig. 13   SALICACEAE, ERICACEAE, EMPETRACEAE
Plants × 4/5; details enlarged.

53

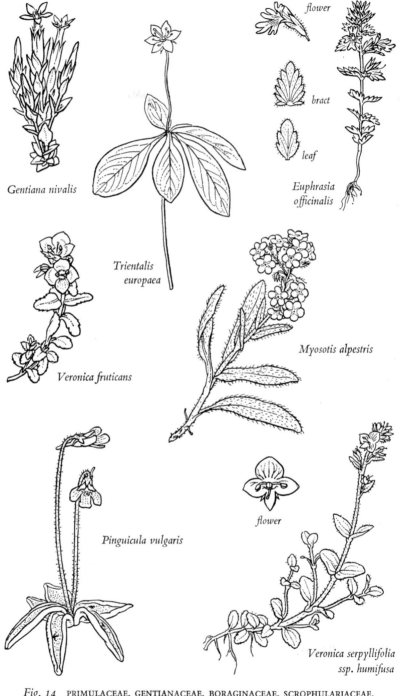

flower

bract

leaf

Gentiana nivalis

Euphrasia
officinalis

Trientalis
europaea

Veronica fruticans

Myosotis alpestris

Pinguicula vulgaris

flower

Veronica serpyllifolia
ssp. humifusa

Fig. 14 PRIMULACEAE, GENTIANACEAE, BORAGINACEAE, SCROPHULARIACEAE,
LENTIBULARIACEAE   *Plants* × 4/5; *details enlarged.*

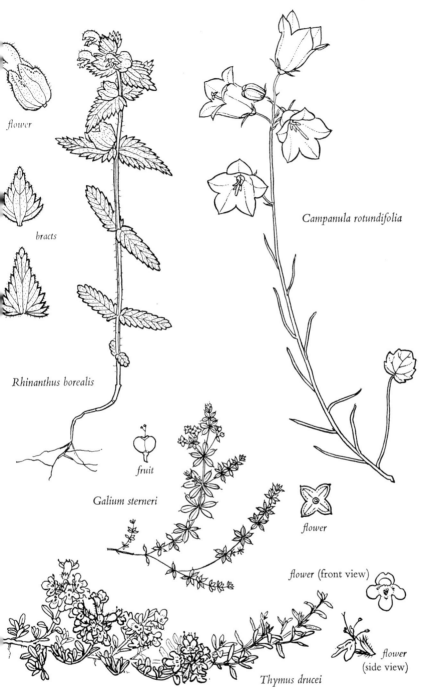

flower

bracts

Rhinanthus borealis

Campanula rotundifolia

fruit

Galium sterneri

flower

flower (front view)

flower
(side view)

Thymus drucei

Fig. 15   SCROPHULARIACEAE, LABIATAE, CAMPANULACEAE, RUBIACEAE
Plants × 4/5; details enlarged.

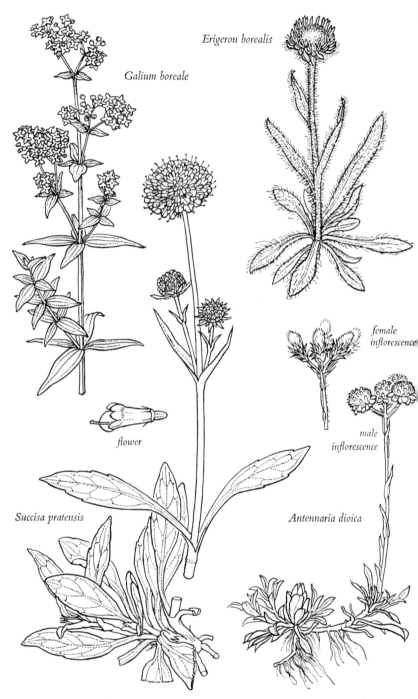

Galium boreale

Erigeron borealis

female inflorescence

male inflorescence

flower

Succisa pratensis

Antennaria dioica

Fig. 16   RUBIACEAE, DIPSACACEAE, COMPOSITAE
Plants × 4/5; details enlarged.

Saussurea alpina

Gnaphalium supinum

flower-head

Hieracium sp.

Fig. 17 COMPOSITAE
Plants × 4/5; *details enlarged.*

57

flower   flower (side view)

Coeloglossum viride

Gymnadenia conopsea

Platanthera chlorantha

Fig. 18   ORCHIDACEAE
Plants × 4/5; details enlarged.

58

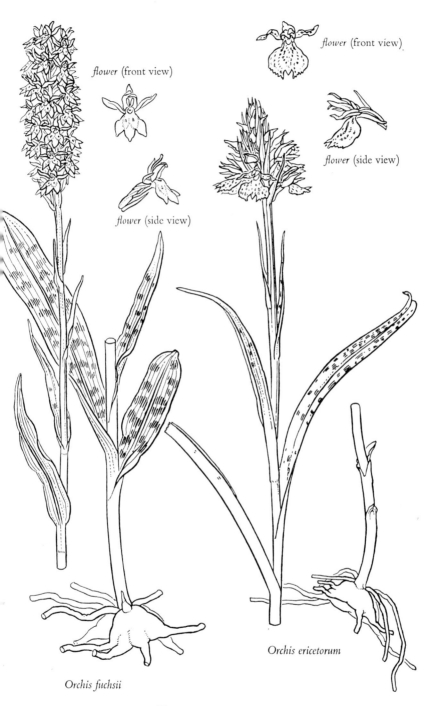

flower (front view)

flower (front view)

flower (side view)

flower (side view)

Orchis ericetorum

Orchis fuchsii

Fig. 19 ORCHIDACEAE
Plants × 4/5; details enlarged.

59

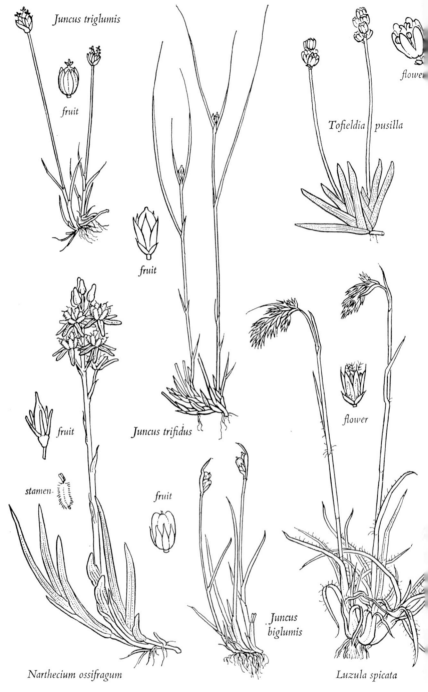

Juncus triglumis

fruit

Tofieldia pusilla

flower

fruit

Narthecium ossifragum

fruit

stamen

Juncus trifidus

fruit

Juncus biglumis

flower

Luzula spicata

Fig. 20 LILIACEAE, JUNCACEAE
Plants × 4/5; details enlarged.

fruit

Carex capillaris

fruit

fruit

Trichophorum caespitosum

Juncus castaneus

Carex atrata

Fig. 21 CYPERACEAE
Plants × 4/5; details enlarged.

61

fruit

Carex microglochin

Carex atrofusca

fruit

fruit

female spike

fruit

male spike

male flower

Carex saxatilis

Carex dioica

Fig. 22 CYPERACEAE
Plants × 4/5; details enlarged.

non-viviparous form

non-viviparous spikelet

spikelet

viviparous spikelet

viviparous form

viviparous spikelet

Sieglingia decumbens

Poa alpina

Festuca vivipara

Fig. 23 GRAMINEAE
Plants × 4/5; details enlarged.

63

spikelet

spikelet

Sesleria caerulea

Anthoxanthum odoratum

Helictotrichon pratense

Fig. 24 GRAMINEAE
Plants × 4/5; details enlarged.

Notes on the Plants Illustrated

In the following brief notes the sequence of species is in accordance with that in the *Flora of the British Isles*, by A. R. Clapham, T. G. Tutin and E. F. Warburg (2nd Edition, Cambridge, 1962). A very useful, concise handbook by the same authors is the *Excursion Flora of the British Isles* (Cambridge, 1959).

For the meaning of botanical terms used in the notes turn to page 85.

LYCOPODIACEAE

Lycopodium selago   Fir Clubmoss (FIG. 1)

Stems erect, 2–10 in. Sporophylls not arranged in a terminal cone. Spores ineffective and reproduction carried out by bud-like gemmae, situated in the axils of leaves. *Habitat*: Moors, heaths and crags, to the summit area. Common.

Lycopodium clavatum   Common Clubmoss, Stag's-horn Clubmoss (FIG. 1)

Stems creeping, 12–40 in. Leaves with long hair-points. Sporophylls in terminal, stalked cones. *Habitat*: Heathy places, to about 2,500 ft. Local.

Lycopodium alpinum   Alpine Clubmoss (FIG. 1)

Stems creeping, 6–20 in. Leaves on branches in 4 rows, appressed, blue-green and without hair-points. Sporophylls in unstalked, solitary cones at end of shoots. *Habitat*: Heathy places, to about 3,700 ft. Frequent at higher altitudes.

SELAGINELLACEAE

Selaginella selaginoides   Lesser Clubmoss (FIG. 1)

Stem creeping, slender, 1–7 in. Leaves arranged spirally, ciliate and with ligule on upper surface. Sporophylls, with sporangia of two kinds (*see fig.*), in unstalked, solitary cones terminating upright branches. *Habitat*: Damp turf often with mosses, to 3,500 ft.

POLYPODIACEAE

Asplenium viride   Green Spleenwort (FIG. 2)

Fronds pinnate, 2–8 in. Stalk blackish at base. Rachis green. Pinnae pale green.

edges toothed. Sori oblong or linear. *Habitat*: Crags and rock crevices, to 3,200 ft.

(*Asplenium trichomanes* Maidenhair Spleenwort. Stalk and rachis blackish.)

Athyrium alpestre Alpine Lady-fern (FIG. 2)

Fronds bi-pinnate, 1–3 ft. Stalk with brown scales. Rachis green or pale purple. Pinnae light green. Differs from *A. filix-femina*, common lady-fern, in having circular sorus without indusium. *Habitat*: Shady rocks and screes, to 3,500 ft.

Cystopteris fragilis Brittle Bladder-fern (FIG. 3)

Rootstock short. Fronds tufted, bi-pinnate, lanceolate, 4–12 in. Longest pinnae about middle of frond. Sori with white, pointed, flap-like indusia. *Habitat*: Shady rocks, to about 3,800 ft.

Cystopteris montana Mountain Bladder-fern (FIG. 3)

Rootstock long, creeping. Fronds on long stalks, triangular, tri-pinnate, 4–12 in. Lowest pinnae much longer than the others, giving frond its distinctive triangular shape. *Habitat*: Damp shaded rocky places, to about 3,000 ft. Rare and very local.

Woodsia alpina Alpine Woodsia (FIG. 3)

Fronds 2–6 in. Rachis, sometimes under-surface of pinnae, sparsely covered with very short brown scales (much denser and longer in *W. ilvensis*). Sori surrounded by indusia, distinctively split up into hair-like segments. *Habitat*: On rocks to about 3,000 ft. Rare, very local.

Polystichum lonchitis Holly Fern (FIG. 2)

Fronds stiff, leathery, simply pinnate, $\frac{1}{2}$–2 ft. Pinnae ovate or ovate-lanceolate with spiny teeth. Sori in rows, with toothed indusia. *Habitat*: Rock crevices which are often deep, to 3,500 ft.

OPHIOGLOSSACEAE

Botrychium lunaria Moonwort (FIG. 3)

Single frond, pinnate, 2–6 in. Pinnae in pairs, broad, without midrib, sterile. Fertile panicle from stalk of frond and overtopping it. *Habitat*: Turf and rocks, to 3,400 ft. Local.

RANUNCULACEAE

Trollius europaeus Globe Flower (FIG. 4)

Stem erect, $1\frac{1}{2}$–2 ft. Leaves palmate. Flowers globular; 5–15 large yellow sepals, enclosing 5–15 narrow nectaries (representing petals), and as many stamens. *Fl.* June–July. *Habitat*: Pastures and ledges, to about 3,000 ft. Local.

Thalictrum alpinum Alpine Meadow Rue (FIG. 4)

Stem erect, slender, 3–6 in. Leaflets whitish beneath. Flowers in a simple raceme.

Perianth of 4 pale purple segments; stamens pendulous, with violet filaments. *Fl.* June–July. *Habitat*: Damp ledges and among rocks. Frequent, up to 3,900 ft.

CRUCIFERAE

Cochlearia alpina (C. officinalis ssp. *alpina)* Alpine Scurvy-grass (FIG. 5)
Stems, spreading or ascending, 2–16 in. Leaves firm, kidney or heart-shaped. Petals white or slightly lilac. Fruit a silicula, narrowing at each end. *Fl.* June–August. *Habitat*: By burns, in flushes, on wet rocks, to 3,800 ft. Local.

Draba norvegica Rock Whitlow Grass (FIG. 4)
Stems 1–2 in., usually leafless, rarely with 1–2 leaves, stellately hairy. Inflorescence with few flowers. Fruit a silicula, *not twisted*. *Fl.* July–August. *Habitat*: Rocks, higher part of mountain. Rare, very local.

Draba incana Hoary Whitlow Grass (FIG. 4)
Stems erect, 3–20 in. Basal and stem leaves, also stems, with both simple and stellate hairs. Inflorescence dense. Petals white. Fruit a silicula, *twisted*. *Fl.* June–July. *Habitat*: Rocky places, to 3,500 ft. Local.

VIOLACEAE

Viola palustris Marsh Violet (FIG. 5)
No aerial stem. Leaves, kidney-shaped, from long, creeping rhizome. Flower lilac with purple streaks; spur blunt, longer than sepal appendages. Fruit on erect stalk. *Fl.* May–August. *Habitat*: Marshy places, to 3,800 ft. Common.

Viola lutea Mountain Pansy (FIG. 5)
Stems, 3–8 in., ascending from slender creeping rhizomes. Leaves, terminal lobe nearly always entire, stipules palmately divided (*see fig.*). Flower large, purple or yellow, or purple and yellow (on Lawers notably purple), but always yellow at base of lowest petal; spur 2–3 times as long as sepal appendages. *Fl.* June–August. *Habitat*: Grassy places and rock ledges. Common locally.

POLYGALACEAE

Polygala serpyllifolia Thyme-leaved Milkwort (FIG. 6)
Stem slender, ascending, 1–10 in. Lower leaves opposite. Flowers 3–8, blue or grey-blue. 2 inner sepals large, concealing fruit. *Fl.* May–August. *Habitat*: Grassy and heathy places, to 3,400 ft. Common.

CARYOPHYLLACEAE

Silene acaulis Moss Campion (FIG. 6)
Stems much branched, in dense tufts, forming cushions 1–3 in. high. Leaves

linear, ciliate near base. Flowers solitary; petals rose pink, sometimes white. *Fl.*
June–August. *Habitat*: Crags and rocky ground, to summit area. Frequent.

Cerastium alpinum   Alpine Mouse-ear Chickweed (FIG. 6)
Stems, to 6 in., and leaves, ovate, both covered long white hairs. Flowers 1–4,
conspicuous, about 1 in. across; petals white, bifid. *Fl.* June–August. *Habitat*:
Rocky places, to 3,900 ft. Local.

Sagina saginoides   Alpine Pearlwort (FIG. 7)
Stems slender, hairless, decumbent then ascending, 1–3 in. Leaves linear, ending
in a bristle. Flowers small on slender stalks; petals white, equalling or rather
shorter than sepals. *Fl.* June–August. *Habitat*: Rocky places, to 3,900 ft. Rare.

(*Sagina intermedia*   Lesser Alpine Pearlwort
Stems forming compact tufts, 1 in. or less in height. Flowers solitary on very
short stalks. *Fl.* June–August. *Habitat*: Rocks on highest parts of mountain. Very
rare.)

Minuartia rubella   Alpine Sandwort (FIG. 6)
Stems densely tufted, 1–2 in. Leaves linear, 3-veined. Flowers usually solitary,
on glandular stalks; sepals acute, 3-veined; petals white, shorter than sepals.
Fl. July–August. *Habitat*: Rocks, to 3,500 ft. Rare and local.

Cherleria sedoides   Mossy Cyphel (FIG. 6)
Stems tufted, plant forming a yellow-green cushion, 1–3 in. high. Leaves linear,
crowded. Flowers usually of separate sexes; sepals yellowish; petals absent or
minute in male flowers. *Fl.* June–August. *Habitat*: Crags and stony places, to
3,900 ft. Local.

LINACEAE

Linum catharticum   Purging Flax (FIG. 6)
Stems wiry, erect, 2–10 in. Leaves opposite, oblong and entire. Flowers in
loosely branched cymes. Petals white. *Fl.* June–September. *Habitat*: Grassy
places, to about 2,700 ft. Common.

GERANIACEAE

Geranium sylvaticum   Wood Cranesbill (FIG. 7)
Stems erect, hairy, 1–2 ft. Leaves palmate, deeply lobed, hairy on both sides.
Flowers in pairs; petals blue-violet. Fruit, beak about 1 in. long with glandular
hairs. *Fl.* June–July. *Habitat*: Moist ledges, to about 3,000 ft. Local.

OXALIDACEAE

Oxalis acetosella   Wood-sorel (FIG. 7)
Creeping rhizome, no aerial stem. Leaves stalked, trifoliate. Flowers solitary.

Flower-stalks 2–5 in.; petals white with lilac or purple veins. *Fl.* June–July. *Habitat*: Among rocks, in shade, to 3,800 ft. Local.

ROSACEAE

Potentilla crantzii   Alpine Cinquefoil (FIG. 8)

Woody, branched rootstock, with flowering stems up to 10 in. Lower leaves stalked, palmate, with 5 toothed leaflets; stem leaves almost stalkless, with 3 leaflets. Flowers in a cyme. Flower-stalks up to $1\frac{1}{2}$ in.; petals 5, golden-yellow, usually with deep orange spot at base. *Fl.* June–July. *Habitat*: Rock ledges to 3,400 ft. Local.

Sibbaldia procumbens   Sibbaldia (FIG. 8)

Rootstock prostrate, 2–6 in., woody, branched. Leaves grey-green, with 3 wedge-shaped leaflets, 3-toothed at apex. Flowers, $\frac{1}{4}$ in. broad, in dense cymes; petals yellow, much smaller than sepals. *Fl.* July–August. *Habitat*: Grassy and rocky places, to 3,700 ft. Local.

Dryas octopetala   Mountain Avens (FIG. 9)

Stem shrubby, creeping, much branched. Leaves crenate, glossy green above, white beneath. Flowers white, $1–1\frac{1}{2}$ in. wide; petals usually 8, styles persistent, feathery in fruit. *Fl.* June–July. *Habitat*: Ledges, to about 2,600 ft. Very local.

Alchemilla alpina   Alpine Lady's Mantle (FIG. 8)

Stems ascending from thick, somewhat creeping stock. Basal leaves deeply palmate; segments 5–7, toothed, grey-green above, silky-white beneath. Flowers in terminal clusters; greenish-yellow; petals absent. *Fl.* June–August. *Habitat*: Grassy places, crags and high ridges, to summit. Abundant.

Alchemilla glabra   Lady's Mantle (FIG. 9)

Stems slightly hairy on lower portions, hairless above. Leaves kidney-shaped, with 7–9 toothed lobes; hairless except in upper portions of veins on under side. Flowers green, in clusters; petals absent. *Fl.* June–August. *Habitat*: Grassland and rock ledges, to summit. Common.

(*Alchemilla filicaulis* and *A. wichurae* also may be found on middle slopes of the mountain.)

CRASSULACEAE

Sedum rosea   Rose-root (FIG. 9)

Stock thick. Stem erect, unbranched, to 12 in. Leaves crowded, fleshy, glaucous, to $1\frac{3}{4}$ in. long. Flowers yellow-green; in dense terminal clusters; male and female on different plants. *Fl.* June–August. *Habitat*: Rocks, to about 3,800 ft.

Sedum villosum   Hairy Stonecrop (FIG. 10)

Stem 2–6 in. Stem and leaves with glandular hairs, pubescent, usually reddish.

Leaves alternate, oblong, fleshy. Flowers terminal or axillary; petals pink. *Fl.* June–July. *Habitat*: Bogs and wet rocks, to 3,600 ft. Very local.

SAXIFRAGACEAE

Saxifraga nivalis   Alpine Saxifrage (FIG. 10)

Stems stiff, leafless, with glandular hairs, 1–6 in. Leaves broadly spathulate, coarsely toothed, purple beneath and forming basal rosette. Flowers in a dense head; greenish-white petals. *Fl.* July–August. *Habitat*: Rocks, to summit. Rare and local.

Saxifraga stellaris   Starry Saxifrage (FIG. 10)

Stems leafless, 2–8 in., with long hairs below, glandular hairs above. Leaves ovate, toothed, forming 1 or more basal rosettes. Flowers in panicles; petals white with 2 yellow spots near base. *Fl.* June–August. *Habitat*: By burns and on wet rocks, to summit. Common.

Saxifraga cernua   Drooping Saxifrage (FIG. 11)

Stem 1–6 in. Leaves palmate, with acute lobes; basal leaves kidney-shaped, stalked; stem leaves almost stalkless, becoming bracts on upper stem with red bulbils in axils in place of flowers. Flower, when present, terminal, solitary, white. *Fl.* July. *Habitat*: Rocks, from about 3,600–3,850 ft. Rare and very local. (Found also on Ben Nevis range and on Bidean nam Bian, Glencoe.)

Saxifraga hypnoides   Mossy Saxifrage (FIG. 10)

Flowering stems erect, 3–6 in., from rosettes of lobed leaves. Numerous sterile, creeping shoots, with 3–5–cleft leaves. Flowers white. *Fl.* June–July. *Habitat*: Rocky slopes, to summit area. Local.

Saxifraga aizoides   Yellow Mountain Saxifrage (FIG. 10)

Sterile stems decumbent; flowering stems erect. Leaves oblong-linear, entire, ciliate. Flowers in loose terminal cyme; petals widely spaced, yellow with orange-yellow spots, rarely orange with orange-red spots. *Fl.* June–August. *Habitat*: By burns and on wet rocks, to about 3,800 ft. Locally common.

Saxifraga oppositifolia   Purple Saxifrage (FIG. 11)

Stem prostate, branched. Leaves opposite, densely packed, obovate, usually ciliate, dark green, thickened at tip, flattened and pitted (*see fig.*). Flowers terminal, solitary; petals purple. *Fl.* April–June. *Habitat*: Wet stony places and moist crags, to summit area. Frequent.

Chrysosplenium oppositifolium   Opposite-leaved Golden Saxifrage (FIG. 11)

Non-flowering stems decumbent and rooting, flowering stems erect, 2–6 in. Leaves opposite, crenate, with scattered hairs. Flowers in terminal cymes, yellow; sepals 4–5; no petals; stamens on prominent disc. *Fl.* May–July. *Habitat:* Wet places, often in shade of rocks, to 3,400 ft. Frequent.

PARNASSIACEAE

Parnassia palustris   Grass of Parnassus (FIG. 11)

Stem erect, 3–8 in. Basal leaves stalked, heart-shaped, pointed; one stalkless leaf on stem. Flowers terminal, solitary; petals white, veined; prominent feature 5 gland-tipped staminodes (*see fig.*). *Fl.* July–September. *Habitat:* Wet places, to 3,300 ft. Local.

ONAGRACEAE

Epilobium anagallidifolium   Alpine Willow-herb (FIG. 12)

Stem slender, 2–4 in., ascending from decumbent base. Leaves lanceolate, shortly stalked, slightly toothed, hairless. Flowers drooping in bud; sepals red; petals pink. *Fl.* July–August. *Habitat:* Wet places, to 3,900 ft. Local.

Epilobium alsinefolium   Chickweed Willow-herb (FIG. 12)

Stem 4–12 in. Leaves ovate, much broader, more pointed and more distinctly toothed than in *E. anagallidifolium*. Flowers drooping; petals bluish-red. *Fl.* July–August. *Habitat:* Wet places, to 3,400 ft. Local.

CORNACEAE

Chamaepericlymenum suecicum   Dwarf Cornel (FIG. 12)

Stem 3–6 in., erect from creeping rhizome. Leaves opposite, ovate, 3–5 veins. Flowers small, purplish-black; in terminal umbel surrounded by 4 conspicuous white bracts. Fruit red. *Fl.* July–August. *Habitat:* Moors, to 2,500 ft. Very local.

POLYGONACEAE

Polygonum viviparum   Viviparous Bistort (FIG. 12)

Stem erect, 3–12 in. Leaves linear-lanceolate, tapering at base, lower leaves stalked, upper leaves sessile; stipules forming a tube. Flowers small, white or pink; in terminal spike, lower part of spike with purple bulbils. *Fl.* June–August. *Habitat:* Grassy slopes and rocks, to summit area. Common.

Oxyria digyna   Mountain Sorrel (FIG. 12)

Stem erect, 2–12 in. Leaves from root-stock, kidney-shaped, fleshy with long stalks. Flowers reddish-green, in leafless panicle. *Fl.* June–August. *Habitat:* Wet rocky places, to 3,900 ft. Local.

SALICACEAE

Salix lapponum   Downy Willow (FIG. 12)

Compact shrub, 1–5 ft. Leaves $\frac{3}{4}$–2 in. long, eliptic or oblong, green with silky hairs above, cottony beneath. Catkin scales with long white hairs. *Fl.* May–July. *Habitat*: Wet rocks, to 3,000 ft. Very local.

Salix arbuscula   Plum-leaved Willow (FIG. 13)

Shrub, 1–2 ft. Leaves $\frac{1}{4}$–$\frac{3}{4}$ in., ovate-lanceolate, more or less serrate, hairless and shining above, glaucous with a few hairs beneath. Catkins lateral on leafy stalks. *Fl.* June–July. *Habitat*: Crags and ledges, to 2,600 ft. Very local.

Salix herbacea   Least Willow (FIG. 13)

Shrub with few branches, about 1 in. long, arising from creeping rhizome. Leaves $\frac{1}{4}$–$\frac{3}{4}$ in. long, broadly ovate, serrate, glabrous, bright green and shining, veins prominent. Catkins terminal, on leafless stalks. *Fl.* June–July. *Habitat*: Higher slopes and ridges, to summit. Common locally.

Salix reticulata   Net-leaved Willow (FIG. 13)

Shrub with branches arising from a creeping rhizome. Leaves $\frac{1}{4}$–2 in. long, rounded or oval, dark green, wrinkled and strongly net-veined above, glaucous beneath. Catkins terminal on long stalks. *Fl.* June–July. *Habitat*: Ledges, to 3,600 ft. Local, rare.

ERICACEAE

Vaccinium vitis-idaea   Cowberry, Red Whortleberry (FIG. 13)

Shrub, to 1 ft., evergreen. Leaves $\frac{1}{4}$–1$\frac{1}{4}$ in., obovate, leathery, shining green above, paler, dotted with glands below. Flowers in terminal, drooping racemes; pinkish-white. Fruit red. *Fl.* June–August. *Habitat*: Moors and crags, to 3,600 ft. Frequent.

Vaccinium uliginosum   Bog Whortleberry (FIG. 13)

Shrub, to 1$\frac{1}{2}$ ft., deciduous. Leaves $\frac{1}{4}$–1 in. long, obovate or oval, blue-green and net-veined. Flowers pale pink. Fruit black with glaucous bloom. *Fl.* May–June. *Habitat*: Moors, to about 3,000 ft. Local.

(*Vaccinium myrtillus*   Blaeberry

Twigs angled. Leaves finely toothed, acute, bright green. Flowers greenish-pink. Fruit black with glaucous bloom. Widespread, to summit area.)

EMPETRACEAE

Empetrum hermaphroditum   Crowberry (FIG. 13)

Shrub $\frac{1}{2}$–1$\frac{1}{2}$ ft. Leaves crowded, oblong, $\frac{1}{4}$ in. long, margins rounded. Flowers hermaphrodite, purple. *Fl.* May–June. *Habitat*: Moors, to about 3,000 ft. Local.

(*Empetrum nigrum*   Common Crowberry

Has parallel-sided leaves and almost always dioecious flowers. *Habitat*: Moors, generally at lower elevations than *E. hermaphroditum*.)

PRIMULACEAE

Trientalis europaea   Chickweed Wintergreen (FIG. 14)

Stem erect, 3–10 in. Leaves, $\frac{1}{2}$–3 in. long, few in whorl at top of stem. Flowers, usually solitary, erect on stalks 2–3 in. long; corolla of 5–9 white, ovate, pointed petals. *Fl.* June–July. *Habitat*: Grassy places, to about 2,600 ft. Local.

GENTIANACEAE

Gentiana nivalis   Small Gentian (FIG. 14)

Annual. Simple or branched stem, erect, 1–6 in. Leaves opposite, ovate or obovate, sometimes in basal rosette. Flowers terminal; corolla bright blue with small lobes between 5 large lobes. *Fl.* July–September. *Habitat*: Crags and rocky slopes, to about 3,500 ft. Rare and local.

(*Gentianella campestris*   Field Gentian

Differs from *G. nivalis* in calyx having 4 lobes, the 2 outer much larger than and overlapping the 2 inner; corolla also differs having usually 4 lilac-blue or whitish lobes and no small lobes between. Common at lower levels.)

BORAGINACEAE

Myosotis alpestris   Alpine Forget-me-not (FIG. 14)

Stem erect, 2–8 in. Leaves oblong-lanceolate, hairy on both sides. Flowers in cymes; corolla blue, $\frac{1}{4}$ in. across with 5 flat, round lobes. *Fl.* July–September. *Habitat*: On crags and in turf, to 3,850 ft. Very local.

SCROPHULARIACEAE

Veronica fruticans   Rock Speedwell (FIG. 14)

Stems 2–3 in., ascending from woody procumbent base. Leaves about $\frac{1}{4}$ in. long, oblong, rather leathery. Flowers in short recemes; corolla 4-lobed, about $\frac{1}{3}$ in. across, deep blue with red ring in centre. *Fl.* July–August. *Habitat*: On rocks, to 3,600 ft. Local.

Veronica serpyllifolia ssp. *humifusa*   Thyme-leaved Speedwell (FIG. 14)

Stem decumbent, rooting. Leaves opposite, almost stalkless, broadly ovate, light green. Flowers few, in short racemes; corolla $\frac{1}{4}$ in. across, with 4 light-blue, purple-veined lobes. *Fl.* June–August. *Habitat*: Wet places, to 3,000 ft. Local.

Rhinanthus borealis   Northern Yellow-rattle (FIG. 15)

Stem hairy, erect, 2–10 in. Leaves oblong, with coarse, rounded teeth; bracts triangular, deeply-cut, acute teeth (*see fig.*). Flowers few, in terminal, leafy spike: calyx inflated, covered with hairs; corolla deep yellow with violet teeth. *Fl.* July–August. *Habitat*; Grassy slopes, to about 3,500 ft. Local.

Euphrasia officinalis spp. Eyebright (FIG. 14)

Annual. Stem more or less branched or unbranched, 1–8 in. Leaves opposite, oval, deeply toothed; bracts larger and broader, more acutely toothed (*see fig.*). Flowers in axils of bracts; corolla open, with 2 lips, lower 3-lobed, whitish tinged red or violet, veins purple, yellow spot on lower lip. *Fl.* June–August. *Habitat*: Heathy and grassy places. Frequent.

Very variable; including several micro-species, of which *E. frigida* reaches the higher slopes.

LENTIBULARIACEAE

Pinguicula vulgaris Common Butterwort (FIG. 14)

Leaves ¾–3 in. long, forming basal rosette, stalkless, ovate-oblong, margin incurved, yellow-green, covered sticky, insect-trapping glands. Flowers solitary, on slender stalks; corolla blue-purple with white patch at mouth, spur long, pointed. *Fl.* June–July. *Habitat*: Boggy places and wet rocks, to about 3,000 ft. Frequent.

LABIATAE

Thymus drucei Thyme (FIG. 15)

Tufted, much branched, with creeping runners. Leaves opposite about ¼ in. long, oval, veins prominent on under surface. Flowering stems hairy on 2 opposite sides. Flowers in dense head, rose purple. *Fl.* June–August. *Habitat*: Heathy places and amongst rocks, to 3,700 ft. Common.

CAMPANULACEAE

Campanula rotundifolia Harebell, Bluebell (FIG. 15)

Stem branched, 6–12 in. Basal leaves long-stalked, round, toothed; lower leaves stalkless, lanceolate; upper leaves linear. Flowers few in raceme, often solitary; corolla blue, rarely whitish. *Fl.* June–August. *Habitat*: Grassy places, to 3,000 ft. Locally common.

RUBIACEAE

Galium boreale Northern Bedstraw (FIG. 16)

Stem 4-angled, 8–18 in., with ascending branches. Leaves lanceolate, 3-veined, ¼–¾ in. long, 4 in whorl. Flowers very small, crowded in spreading panicle; corolla white with 4 ovate, apiculate lobes. *Fl.* July–August. *Habitat*: Rocky places, to 3,500 ft. Local.

Galium sterneri Slender Bedstraw (FIG. 15)

Stem 4-angled, slender, 2–6 in., with ascending branches. Leaves about ¼ in. long, narrow, broadest near sharp tip, 1-veined, 6–8 in whorl. Flowers in loose panicle; corolla, 4 cream-white acuminate lobes. *Fl.* June–July. *Habitat*: Grassy slopes, rocky places, to about 2,200 ft. Frequent locally.

DIPSACACEAE

Succisa pratensis   Devil's-bit Scabious (FIG. 16)

Stems $\frac{1}{2}$–2 ft., ascending from short, thick, truncate root-stock. Leaves opposite, lanceolate; basal leaves to 1 ft. long. Flowers in round heads; corolla 4-lobed, mauve-purple. *Fl.* July–September. *Habitat*: Damp grassy places, to 2,700 ft. Frequent.

COMPOSITAE

Gnaphalium supinum   Dwarf Cudweed (FIG. 17)

Stems 1–4 in., from creeping, branched root-stock. Leaves grey-green, linear, acute, woolly. Flower-heads 1–7, in short terminal spike; bracts grey, with brown, scarious margins. *Fl.* July. *Habitat*: Rocky places, to summit area. Frequent.

Antennaria dioica   Mountain Everlasting, Cat's-foot (FIG. 16)

Leafy stolons from creeping woody root-stock. Flowering stems 2–8 in. Leaves narrow lanceolate, acute, $\frac{1}{4}$–2 in. long, woolly beneath. Flower-heads short-stalked in terminal umbel; bracts, white and spreading on male heads, rose-pink and erect on female heads. *Fl.* June–July. *Habitat*: Heathy places, to 2,800 ft. Local.

Erigeron borealis   Boreal Fleabane (FIG. 16)

Stems hairy, erect, 3–8 in., from short, creeping root-stock. Leaves mostly basal, lanceolate, tapering to base, $\frac{3}{4}$–1$\frac{1}{2}$ in. long. Flower-heads usually solitary; ray florets purple, disc florets yellow. *Fl.* July–August. *Habitat*: Ledges, to 3,500 ft. Rare and local.

Saussurea alpina   Alpine Saussurea (FIG. 17)

Stem erect, grooved, cottony, 3–15 in. Leaves lanceolate, serrate, white-cottony beneath. Heads cylindrical, terminal, clustered, scented; florets purple, exceeding bracts. *Fl.* July–September. *Habitat*: Ledges, to 3,850 ft. Local.

Hieracium spp.   Hawkweed (FIG. 17)

The various Hawkweeds often require critical study for identification. They are usually $\frac{1}{2}$–1$\frac{1}{2}$ ft., have several basal leaves, few stem leaves and attractive bright yellow heads. *Fl.* Late summer. *Habitat*: Crags and ledges, to about 3,500 ft.

LILIACEAE

Tofieldia pusilla   Scottish Asphodel (FIG. 20)

Flowering stem slender, 3–8 in., from basal cluster of leaves, which are linear,

flat, stiff and pointed. Flowers terminal, in dense raceme, greenish-white. *Fl.*
June–August. *Habitat*: Wet places, to 2,700 ft. Local.

Narthecium ossifragum   Bog Asphodel (FIG. 20)

Flowering stems 6–12 in., from creeping root-stock. Leaves broadly linear,
acute, stiff, usually curved. Flowers stalked, in compact racemes; perianth segments spreading, acute, deep yellow; stamens with woolly filaments, orange
anthers. *Fl.* July–September. *Habitat*: Boggy places, to 3,000 ft. Common
locally.

JUNCACEAE

Juncus trifidus   Three-leaved Rush (FIG. 20)

Stem erect, 6–12 in., wiry, round. Leaves mostly reduced to sheaths. Flowers
1–3, in axils of 2–3 thread-like bracts; perianth segments dark chestnut-brown.
Fl. June–August. *Habitat*: Ledges and exposed ridges to summit area. Frequent.

Juncus castaneus   Chestnut Rush (FIG. 21)

Stem 4–12 in. Leaves 2–8 in., grooved above, with long sheathing base. Flowers
large, terminal, in small dense heads, dark chestnut brown. *Fl.* June–July.
Habitat: Wet, often peaty places, to 3,200 ft. Rare and local.

Iuncus biglumis   Two-flowered Rush (FIG. 20)

Stem erect, 2–5 in., grooved along one side. Leaves all basal, 1–2 in. curved.
Flowers terminal, usually in pairs one above the other, and usually overtopped
by bract; perianth segments purple-brown. *Fl.* June–July. *Habitat*: Wet, rather
stony flushes, to 3,100 ft. Rare and local.

Juncus triglumis   Three-flowered Rush (FIG. 20)

Stem erect, stiff, 2–10 in., round. Leaves all basal, curved, 1–4 in. Flowers
terminal, 2–3, usually on one level not overtopped by lowest bract; perianth
segments light reddish-brown. *Fl.* June–July. *Habitat*: Wet places, to 3,000 ft.
Local.

Luzula spicata   Spiked Woodrush (FIG. 20)

Stem 1–9 in. Leaves linear, curved, grooved. Flowers terminal, in drooping
spike-like inflorescence, chestnut-brown. *Fl.* June–July. *Habitat*: Rocky places,
to 3,900 ft. Local.

ORCHIDACEAE

Coeloglossum viride   Frog Orchid (FIG. 18)

Stem 3–12 in. Leaves lanceolate. Flowers in spike, green, striped with red;
sepals hooded, lip acutely 3-lobed (centre lobe small). *Fl.* June–August.
Habitat: Grassy places and ledges, to 3,000 ft. Local.

Gymnadenia conopsea   Fragrant Orchid (FIG. 18)

Stem 6–15 in. Leaves long, narrow, keeled. Flowers, reddish-lilac, in dense, spike, strongly scented; lateral sepals spreading; spur long, very slender. *Fl.* June–August. *Habitat*: Grassy places, to 2,000 ft. Locally common.

Platanthera chlorantha   Greater Butterfly Orchid (FIG. 18)

Stem 9–20 in. Lower leaves 2, large, elliptical, shining. Flowers in pyramidal lax spike, greenish-white, large, strongly scented; sepals spreading; spur long; pollen-masses diverging. *Fl.* June–July. *Habitat*: Grassy pastures on lower slopes, usually below 1,000 ft. Local.

Orchis ericetorum (*Dactylorchis maculata* ssp. *ericetorum*)   Heath Spotted Orchid (FIG. 19)

Stem 6–20 in. Leaves keeled and folded, all lanceolate, spots, if present, circular. Flower with 3-lobed lip, middle lobe much smaller and narrower than lateral lobes; pink or white, marked many reddish dots. *Fl.* June–August. *Habitat*: Acid heathland, to 3,000 ft. Locally common.

Orchis fuchsii (*Dactylorchis fuchsii*)   Spotted Orchid (FIG. 19)

Stem 6–10 in. Leaves keeled, lowest rather broad, blunt, upper narrowly lanceolate, pointed, sometimes unspotted but transversely elongated, dark blotches usual. Flowers in rather long, cylindrical spike; lip almost equally divided into 3 lobes, central lobe triangular, pointed; pink or white with reddish lines. *Fl.* June–August. *Habitat*: Grassy places, on base-rich lower slopes only. Frequent.

CYPERACEAE

Trichophorum caespitosum   Deer Grass (FIG. 21)

Stems 2–14 in., tufted, round, smooth, yellowish-brown when old. Uppermost sheath only with short leaf-blade, lower sheaths light brown, shining. Flowers in solitary terminal spikelet, 3-flowered, brown. *Fl.* May–June. *Habitat*: Heaths, boggy places, to about 3,000 ft. Common.

Carex capillaris   Hair Sedge (FIG. 21)

Stems 4–8 in., tufted. Leaves mostly from base, short, flat, recurved. Flowers in spikes, with fine hair-like stalks, male spike usually overtopped by female spikes; pale yellowish green. *Fl.* July. *Habitat*: Wet grassy slopes, crags, to 2,800 ft. Local.

Carex saxatilis   Russet Sedge (FIG. 22)

Stem 6–12 in. Leaves concave, narrow, with very short, blunt ligule: lower leaf-sheaths persistent. Flower spikes ovoid, male dark purple, female purplish-brown, the upper almost stalkless. *Fl.* July. *Habitat*: Boggy places, to about 3,500 ft. Very local.

Carex atrata   Black Sedge (FIG. 21)

Stem 1–1½ ft., strongly 3-angled, usually drooping at top. Leaves keeled, grey-green, lower sheaths persistent, dark brown. Flowers in black, flattish, stalked spikes; lowest bract leaflike, often overtopping highest spike. *Fl.* June–July. *Habitat*: Ledges, to 3,100 ft. Local, rather rare.

Carex atrofusca   Scorched Sedge (FIG. 22)

Stem 4–14 in. Leaves almost flat, much shorter than stem, lower sheaths not persistent. Female flower-spikes ovoid, often touching each other, nodding on very slender stalks; glumes purple-black with pale midrib. *Fl.* July. *Habitat*: Boggy places, over 2,500 ft. Very local and rare.

Carex microglochin   Small Bristle Sedge (FIG. 22)

Stem erect, 3–4 in. from shortly creeping rhizome. Leaves almost flat, shorter than stem. Spike terminal, about ¼ in. long; male glumes lanceolate, female glumes (soon falling) ovate with very thin tips, both reddish-brown with pale midribs. Fruits narrowly conical, yellowish, turned downwards, with stout bristle protruding with stigmas. *Fl.* July–August. *Habitat*: Boggy places, 2,500–2,700 ft. Very local and rare.

Carex dioica   Dioecious Sedge (FIG. 22)

Stem erect, round, stiff, 4–6 in. Leaves grooved, shorter than stem. Spikes terminal, brown, male and female on separate plants; glumes of narrow, male spike soon falling, those of female spike persistent. Fruits ovoid, compressed, spreading or deflexed, greenish-brown with dark brown nerves and long, toothed, notched beak. *Fl.* May–June. *Habitat*: Wet, usually peaty places, to 2,800 ft. Local.

GRAMINEAE

Sieglingia decumbens   Heath Grass (FIG. 23)

Stems 4–20 in., tufted, erect, slender, slightly hairy. Leaves hairless above, dark green beneath; ring of hairs at mouth of leaf sheath. Panicle narrow, erect, ¾–2 in. long; spikelets ovate, purplish or green. *Fl.* July–August. *Habitat*: Heathy places, to about 1,600 ft. Frequent.

Festuca vivipara   Viviparous Sheep's Fescue (FIG. 23)

Stem 3–12 in. Leaves narrow, inrolled, with sheaths split more than halfway to base. Panicle narrow, with many green or purplish spikelets. Flowers replaced by leafy bulbils. *Fl.* June–August. *Habitat*: Grassy places, to summit area. Common.

Poa alpina   Alpine Meadow-grass (FIG. 23)

Stems tufted, erect, 4–16 in., from stout root-stock bearing remains of basal leaves and sheaths. Leaves stiff, broad, contracted abruptly and folded at the tip or throughout. Panicle spreading, with 1–2 branches together; spikelets green or purplish, commonly viviparous. *Fl.* July–August. *Habitat*: Ledges, to about 3,900 ft.

Sesleria caerulea (S. albicans)   Blue Moor-grass (FIG. 24)

Stem stiff, 6–16 in., from creeping root-stock. Leaves blue-grey, flat, keeled, rough on margin, tip sharply pointed. Panicle ovoid, compact, blue-grey, glistening, with small scale at base. Spikelets compressed, with few flowers. *Fl.* May–June. *Habitat*: Crags and grassy places, favouring highly calcareous schists, to 3,000 ft. Local.

Helictotrichon pratense   Meadow Oat (FIG. 24)

Stem erect, 1–2 ft., hairless. Leaves blue-green, stiff, grooved, blunt-tipped, basal spreading. Panicle narrow, lower branches 1–2 together. Spikelets purplish-green, silvery sheen, short-stalked; flowers with bent awns. *Fl.* June–July. *Habitat*: Crags, to 2,700 ft. Local.

Anthoxanthum odoratum   Sweet Vernal-grass (FIG. 24)

Stems tufted, 8–20 in., with scent of coumarin. Leaves flat, short and slightly hairy. Panicle oblong, compact, slightly branched below. Spikelets with hairy glumes, somewhat purplish; flowers with awns. *Fl.* May–June. *Habitat*: Pastures and heathland, to 3,300 ft. Abundant.

Animals of the Mountain

WHILE BEN LAWERS is undoubtedly the most famous mountain in Britain from the botanist's point of view it also presents much of interest to the zoologist, particularly as regards its invertebrate fauna which still requires thorough investigation.

INVERTEBRATES

INSECTS

Numerous species of insects are directly associated with the flora as flower-visitors, plant-feeders or gall-formers, and many others occur as parasites on their fellow insects. The following butterflies and moths, *Lepidoptera*, are frequent:

BUTTERFLIES

Small Ringlet, *Erebia epiphron*.
Meadow Brown, *Maniola jurtina*.
Small Heath, *Coenonympha pamphilus*.
Large Heath, *Coenonympha tullia*.

MOTHS

Northern Eggar, *Lasiocampa quercus*.
Fox Moth, *Macrothyglacia rubi*.
Emperor Moth, *Saturnia pavonia*.
Yellow Underwing, *Anarta myrtilli*.

Less conspicuous perhaps, but generally more abundant, are other insect groups: beetles, *Coleoptera*; true flies, *Diptera*; bugs, *Hemiptera*; and the *Hymenoptera*, that is bees, wasps, ants, sawflies, ichneumon flies, etc.

OTHER INVERTEBRATES

Spiders, many species in all, are frequent on most parts of the mountain, while molluscs are found at all elevations up to at least 3,800 ft.

Although it is hardly possible in this short chapter to do more than refer briefly to the extensive invertebrate fauna of the mountain, the vertebrates may be listed more adequately.

VERTEBRATES

FISHES AND AMPHIBIANS

Brown trout, *Salmo trutta*, inhabit the larger streams and Lochan a Chait. The common frog, *Rana temporaria temporaria*, is very frequent on the wetter slopes and the common toad, *Bufo bufo bufo*, occurs rather less frequently in similar habitats.

Birds and Mammals recorded for the mountain include:

BIRDS

Golden Eagle, *Aquila chrysaetos*. Occasional.
Buzzard, *Buteo buteo*. Frequent.
Sparrow-hawk, *Accipiter nisus*. Occasionally in pursuit of meadow pipits and other small birds.
Peregrine Falcon, *Falco peregrinus*. Occasionally seen, sometimes in pairs over the higher crags.
Merlin, *Falco columbarius*. Occasional.
Kestrel, *Falco tinnunculus*. Common.
Red Grouse, *Lagopus scoticus*. Common.
Ptarmigan, *Lagopus mutus*. On higher parts of the mountain.
Golden Plover, *Charadrius apricarius*. Occasional.
Curlew, *Numenius arquata*. Frequent.
Cuckoo, *Cuculus canorus*. Frequent.
Short-eared Owl, *Asio flammeus*. Occasional.
Swift, *Apus apus*. Frequent in summer over the highest parts of the mountain.
Skylark, *Alauda arvensis*. Common.
Raven, *Corvus corax*. Occasionally over the higher parts of the mountain.
Carrion Crow, *Corvus corone*. Frequent.
Hooded Crow, *Corvus cornix*. Frequent.
Wren, *Troglodytes troglodytes*. Frequent.
Dipper, *Cinclus cinclus*. Occasionally by lower streams.
Fieldfare, *Turdus pilaris*. As winter migrant, visiting lower slopes.
Redwing, *Turdus musicus*. As a winter migrant, visiting lower slopes.
Ring Ouzel, *Turdus torquatus*. Frequenting the higher parts of the mountain, has nested near the summit.
Wheatear, *Oenanthe oenanthe*. Common.
Stonechat, *Saxicola torquata*. Occasional.
Whinchat, *Saxicola rubetra*. Occasional.
Meadow Pipit, *Anthus pratensis*. Very common.
Twite, *Carduelis flavirostris*. Occasional, decreasing in the area.
Snow Bunting, *Plectrophenax nivalis*. Occasionally as migrants.

MAMMALS

Hedgehog, *Erinaceus europaeus*. On lower slopes only.
Mole, *Talpa europaea*. Frequent locally.

Common Shrew, *Sorex araneus castaneus*. May reach the highest parts of the mountain.

Pipistrelle, *Pipistrellus pipistrellus*. Over the lower slopes only.

Fox, *Vulpes vulpes crucigera*. Frequent on all parts of the mountain.

Stoat, *Mustela erminea stabilis*. Frequent on lower slopes.

Weasel, *Mustela nivalis*. Frequent on lower slopes.

Badger, *Meles meles*. Mainly in woods on lower slopes.

Otter, *Lutra lutra*. Usually at lower elevation but probably ascends to Lochan a Chait.

Scottish Wild Cat, *Felis silvestris grampia*. Occasionally observed on the mountain.

Red Deer, *Cervus elaphus scoticus*. Frequent.

Roe Deer, *Capreolus capreolus*. Frequent.

Brown Hare, *Lepus europaeus occidentalis*. Confined to lower slopes.

Scottish Mountain Hare, *Lepus timidus scoticus*. On the higher parts of the mountain.

Rabbit, *Oryctolagus cuniculus*. On the lower slopes only.

Field Mouse, *Apodemus sylvaticus sylvaticus*. Frequent.

Scottish Field Vole, *Microtus agrestis neglectus*. Occasionally seen.

Ski-ing on Ben Lawers range

ONCE A MAJOR CENTRE of Scottish ski-ing, the Lawers area has not been developed as extensively as the other main snowfields in the Cairngorms, Glencoe and Glenshee. It remains, however, a convenient rendezvous for weekend Lowland ski-ers, and it usually offers good prospects for sport early in the season.

Ben Lawers, its Munro brethren Ben Ghlas and Meall Corranaich, and its cousins, the Tarmachans, with slopes almost entirely grass-covered and comparatively free from rock provide reasonable ski-ing conditions with a modest covering of snow. Ben Lawers itself, whose summit only falls short of the 4,000 ft. mark by 16 feet, is not a particularly good ski-ing mountain. Its slopes are convex and it receives the full blast of the nor'-easter early in the winter, converting whatever precipitation manages to cling there into corrugated ice from which later snowfalls soon glissade on to the lower ground. Ben Ghlas and Meall Corranaich, on the other hand, provide conditions to suit every ski-er. The southern slopes of the former are of even gradient and suited to beginners, while the gullies dropping into Coire Odhar from the ridges of Sron Dha Murchdi and Meall Corranaich call for the rapid parallel swung christianias of an experienced ski-er.

The approach to the ski-ing area is by the Lochan na Lairige hill road which climbs up from Loch Tayside to a car park at 1,400 ft. Ski-ers are justly indebted to the National Trust for Scotland for providing this substantial car park. It was constructed in 1952 with the assistance and co-operation of the North of Scotland Hydro-Electric Board and the Cementation Company Ltd., and makes an excellent base for a day's ski-ing. The next stage is to the Scottish Ski Club lunch-hut in Coire Odhar, a distance of some 2 miles, which can only be reached by a climb on foot—or better, on skins. The hut, which was erected in 1932, stands at about 2,400 ft. above sea-level and 200 ft. below the col between Ben Ghlas and Meall Corranaich. It has cooking facilities and is a First-Aid Post of the Mountain Rescue Committee. One can be resting at the hut in sunshine and amid snow only four hours after leaving the smoke and greyness of Edinburgh or Glasgow.

This area has long been a haunt of the Scottish Ski Club whose varied activities are reflected in such topographical nomenclature as 'Higginbotham's Rock', 'Charlie's Gulley', 'Secret Valley' and the 'Gents Burn'.

The Lawers range lacks the long snow-holding type of corrie that is so valuable in Scotland. So long as snow-falls continue it offers some of the best ski-ing, but it never builds up the enduring type of snow-corrie that is found, for instance, in the Cairngorms. The district is, however, clearly suited for ski-touring and Coire Odhar is a good starting-point for this. The summit of Meall Corranaich can be reached by a steep traverse from the col and the concave slopes on the north-west side holds snow well and give runs of over 1,000 ft. in descent. A mile north along its ridge there is usually excellent ski-ing in Coire Gorm between Meall a Choire Leith and Meall Corranaich. This descent continues to Gleann dha-Eigg and is known as 'Charlie's Gulley'. The col between Ben Ghlas and Ben Lawers provides a good vantage point for picking a descent on that side and generally snow will lie well in Coire Chonnaidh and Coire an Tuim Bhric, and if the conditions are good enough the run can be continued by Upper Carie to the Loch Tayside road.

The snow conditions are likely to be suitable for long ski runs on the Lawers range at some time during January and February, but the Scottish climate being notoriously fickle, the time cannot be more accurately predicted. A detailed description of runs, on and off the piste, is given in the official Ski Club publication 'Ski-ing in Scotland'.

List of Botanical Terms

anther: the part of a stamen containing pollen.

apiculate: ending in a short point.

awn: a bristle or hair-like point on the flowers of grasses.

axil: the angle between a leaf and stem.

bifid: split deeply in two.

bract: the leaf in whose axil a flower arises.

bulbil: a little bulb; usually replacing a flower and serving for vegetative spread.

calyx: the collective term for the outermost, usually green, parts of a flower.

ciliate: fringed with long hairs.

corolla: the collective term for the petals of a flower; usually coloured.

crenate: with rounded shallow teeth.

cyme: an inflorescence in which the main axis terminates in a flower.

dioecious: with male and female flowers on separate plants.

entire: without marginal notches.

filament: the stalk of a stamen.

floret: an individual flower of the head as in the Compositae. (Ray florets are white, disc florets yellow in the Daisy).

gemma: a bud which becomes detached and serves for vegetative spread.

glabrous: smooth (without hairs).

glaucous: covered with a whitish bloom like a plum.

glumes: the scale-like parts enclosing the flower in the grasses.

hermaphrodite: with male and female organs in the same flower.

indusium: the covering of the sorus of ferns.

lanceolate: at least 3 times as long as broad, tapering gradually.

ligule: a scale at the top of the leaf sheath in grasses.

nectary: a gland secreting sugary fluids.

obovate: inverted egg-shaped—the broader part above.

ovate: egg-shaped.

palmate: spread out like a fan.

panicle: a branched inflorescence.

perianth: a collective term for petals and sepals.

pinnate: with leaflets (pinnae) on either side of a stalk, like a feather.

pinnules: the smallest leaflets of a much-divided leaf.

raceme: an inflorescence with a main stem that grows on bearing flowers in succession from below upwards.

rachis: the central stalk of a compound leaf.

rhizome: an underground, usually thickened, creeping stem.

scarious: thin and papery in texture.

sepal: the outermost, usually green, parts of a flower.

serrate: with an edge toothed like a saw.

sheath: the basal part of a grass or sedge leaf, tube-like and enclosing the stem.

silicula: a fruit of Cruciferae usually not more than twice as long as broad.

sorus: a cluster of spore-cases of ferns.

spike: a raceme (q.v.) with stalkless flowers.

sporangia: spore cases (of ferns, horsetails and club mosses).

sporophyll: a leaf bearing sporangia (q.v.).

stellate (hairs): with radiating branches like a star.

staminode: a sterile stamen.

stipule: small leaflets at the base of a petiole.

style: the more or less elongate stalk on top of the ovary.

whorl: three or more leaves at one level on a stem in a circle.

The National Trust for Scotland

This Trust is an independent body founded in 1931 to promote the preservation of places of interest in Scotland. It is supported entirely by voluntary contributions—legacies, donations and the subscriptions of members. Membership of the Trust is open to everyone, and this gives free admission to all properties of the Trust, and to properties of the National Trust in England, Wales and Northern Ireland. The life membership subscription of the Trust is £40 (£50 for husband and wife); ordinary membership a minimum of £2 annually. Family membership £3 annually, covers families including all children under 18 years of age. Junior membership, under 21 years of age, is 50p annually. If you wish to become a member of the Trust, or to have further details of its work and the properties under its care, write for free illustrated booklet to –

The Director, The National Trust for Scotland,
5 Charlotte Square, Edinburgh EH2 4DU

TEL. 031-225 2184